WHAT DO YOU WANT T

Searching for a career pivot? Lc
The question of "what you war.
where you are on your career jo

The women of *Finish the Sentence* understand ...

Claire and Bryn – led successful careers before leaving to start
their families. With kids in school full-time, they want to go back
to work. What do they do? How will they get started?

Colleen – an accomplished non-profit leader with a satisfying life
and a wonderful partner. She wants to do more, and make bigger
things happen, but how does she figure out what this means?

Diana – a single mom that dreams of having her own business,
tied to a charitable cause. How does she decide to take this leap
and trust that a net will be there if she falls?

Claudia – a corporate executive with a strong resume that loves
volunteering her time. What is the valuable lesson she must learn
about managing her ego and its impact on her life?

Madeline – the serial entrepreneur, ready to share her success
and connect women with kick ass careers. She's passionate about
what she does but is haunted by something from her past. What
will happen once she re-visits this ghost?

Join these women on their shared journey to change their lives –
and learn the exercises, tools, and best practices they use to
unlock their power and discover career success.

Finish the Sentence

Finish the Sentence

A BUSINESS FABLE ABOUT WOMEN
UNLOCKING THEIR POWER
AND DISCOVERING
CAREER SUCCESS

SHARAN KUYAWA HILDEBRAND

MT PRESS
CHICAGO

Sharan Kuyawa Hildebrand   ... or contact us online at ...
Fearless Sisters LLC   www.FearlessSistersConnect.com
Attn: Permissions
207 East Ohio Street, Suite 117
Chicago, IL 60611

Published in the United States by MT Press,
an imprint of Maker Turtle LLC

ISBN: 978-1-951071-07-3 (e-Book)
ISBN: 978-1-951071-13-4 (Paperback)
ISBN: 978-1-951071-17-2 (Hardback)

Library of Congress Control Number: 2022912966

Cover Design: Sharan Hildebrand
Interior Design: James P. MacLennan

Printing History:
        September 17, 2022   Version 1.0 - First Edition

*No one can make you feel inferior
without your consent.*

- Eleanor Roosevelt

This book is dedicated to my lifelong friends:

Jennifer Blattner

Marijo Calacci

Juel Hood

Rose Fekech

Susan Macek

Sandra Riordan

Thank you for the support, joy and love you've brought to my life all these years.

And to Lydia Ann Kuyawa and Bettie Jean Kuyawa. Two of the strongest and inspirational women I will ever know.

Contents

Introduction

Thank you for picking up my labor of love. When I set out to write *Finish the Sentence*, I had no idea where the journey of writing my first book would take me. Creating stories of six women who are at different stages of their career was soul filling and fun. The lessons they learn, and practices they use to identify what their next career step should be, are all based on my personal life experiences. I have been blessed with many defining moments over the course of my career and sharing them with you is pure joy.

My professional resume includes a history of jobs that other people thought I should do. At times, these roles did not challenge my skills or feed my soul, which usually left me longing for more. I've always loved looking for different ways to communicate the value of a product or service, and would regularly present "the next big thing" to whoever was managing me at the time. My feedback often included a half-hearted nod of support or a low energy approval. These weren't the reactions I was looking for, so I allowed my confidence to drop over potential fear of failure, leaving my ideas to die on the vine.

Finally, I got the feedback I needed. It was a manager later in my career that sat me down, looked me in the eye and gave it to me straight. "Sharan you have such great ideas, but you need to follow through... you need to land the plane... you need to *finish the sentence!*" That conversation changed my outlook and my life and served as the inspiration for this book.

My hope is that you connect with one or more of the women in this story, as they define the next stage of their own careers and finish their own sentences. Let their stories help you further define what you want to be when you grow up and become a role model for the next generation of female leader! Let's build a fearless sisterhood of love and support!

Thank you for sharing this journey with me as publishing this book is the first of many sentences I look forward to finishing. I'm grateful that you're here and hope you find insight and inspiration in these pages.

1

The Event

"God, this room looks amazing!" Claudia exclaimed as she took in the perfectly spaced chairs, pastel tablecloths, and fresh flower arrangements that filled the event space. "The décor and color palette turned out beautifully. It's warm, cozy, and very cheery."

"I agree; the volunteers did a fantastic job of setting everything up; this venue has always been a favorite of mine," Colleen replied. As the two women walked from the back of the hall where their first women's leadership event was being held, they went out of their way to talk with each volunteer they passed. They were grateful for the attention they were paying to placing the finishing touches on the room.

"Hi, thank you for everything that you've done this past week," Claudia said to one of the volunteers, who was adjusting a centerpiece at one of the tables.

"It's my pleasure," the volunteer replied as she turned to Claudia with a smile on her face. "Campbell House changed my life and saved my daughter and me from a horrible future. The support and love we received at the women's shelter is something I will never forget. Volunteering is now a very big deal for me because I get the chance to bring my daughter and teach her how important giving back is."

"What a beautiful idea," Claudia replied.

"Thanks," the woman responded, still smiling brightly. "This event is just another example of the great opportunities Campbell House creates for women; I mean...launching a free program that helps women find a job and build a career is so important. Don't get me wrong, even though this program wasn't available when I was at Campbell House, the counselors were still awesome. I know they're limited in how many people they can help at one time. I'm thinking this program you're going to launch today will really help service more residents while they figure out what they want to be when they grow up!" Claudia loved her spirit and enjoyed sharing a quick laugh before hearing her name being called from the stage.

"Claudia! Hey, it's time to open the doors so people can start to get seated." Claudia gave a thumbs up and asked the woman she was talking with to assist with the doors before she had to head backstage. "Of course!" she replied, and the two parted ways.

Once backstage, Claudia walked to where she could see Colleen and their MC for the day, standing together. The two were reviewing notecards as the MC was making sure that she was pronouncing each speaker's name correctly. "You know, I've known their first names for so long, but not their last!" she exclaimed when she noticed the man working the audio for the event walk toward her.

"Do you mind if we check your mic one more time before we get started?" he asked.

"Not at all...maybe if it doesn't work, they won't hear me mess up," she replied.

Colleen put her hands on the MC's shoulders, "You're going to be great; I know you're nervous, but you're so well-rehearsed. Heck, I bet we'll have to drag you off that stage once you get started as you'll be having so much fun!"

Everyone laughed, then heard the audio man, who was now standing next to a curtain speak out, "I'm going to count down from five, then point to you, which will be your cue to walk out and start the introductions." The MC nodded.

Moments later, with the point of the audio man's finger, she walked onto the stage to launch the event. She had never done anything like this before and was surprised at how calm she felt. *Maybe they will have to drag me off the stage, after all,* she thought to herself, as she felt a smile spread across her face. "Welcome, everyone, and thank you for joining us today!"

With her notecards in hand, she carried on and shared the agenda for the event. "We have an amazing group of women that will be delivering a set of enlightening talks for you, where they'll share best practices and personal lessons learned that shaped their careers and influenced who they are today. You're going to hear about an exercise called the Homework Assignment that can help you design what you want your future to look like, including the type of career you want. We'll then move on and hear about a practice called the Accountability Log that you share with a partner, and that will help you set, review, and achieve your goals each week. Next is an incredible message about leadership that you'll be able to apply not only to your professional life but to your personal life as well. It's called Lead from the Bench. Our last two speakers will talk about the importance of networking, and you'll hear about the power of completing a Dream Network exercise, followed by leveraging your network to create a Personal Board of Directors. All of these women started their career journey at different times and from different places. They're going to share stories of how they struggled with managing their time both personally and professionally. You'll hear how they stopped their career journeys out of fear and always felt like things were left unfinished. You'll also learn about the tools they used to create a network and, ultimately, a plan that helped them find their dream career. I hope you share my excitement about the amazing agenda!" *One more section to cover,* she thought to herself as she flipped to the next notecard.

"Before we get started, I'd like to provide you with some additional information about the mission and vision of Campbell House. Eleanor Campbell founded Campbell House in 1979 after counseling women for years in her social work practice. She wanted to provide a safe place for women in need to stay and find their independence. Today we've been brought together to celebrate the announcement of a new program at Campbell House called Campbell Connected, that's destined to change the lives of many. I know some of you in the audience are still residents of Campbell House, and I'm very excited for you and what you will learn today. But for those of you that aren't familiar with

Campbell House, I'd like to take the next few minutes to tell you more and would like to begin with my own personal story." The MC went on to share the history of the women's shelter and how it had grown and helped hundreds of women over the past few decades to get back on their feet after fleeing abusive relationships and, at times, homelessness. As she flipped to her last note card, the stage lit up from the glow of the screen behind her, displaying a slide. "Before we announce our first speakers, we would like to thank our sponsors, without whom this event would not have been possible. Please join me in a round of applause for these amazing companies and donors." The room clapped and then quieted down as the slide faded, and a spotlight was now focused on two upholstered chairs in the center of the stage.

"Our first talk will be presented by two amazing women who will share how completing an exercise called, The Homework Assignment changed their career paths and futures and eventually brought them to where they are today. Please welcome, Claire Stanley and Bryn Miles." As Claire and Bryn came on stage, they crossed paths with the MC and shared a fist bump. The MC knew these women and the rest of the speakers scheduled to present that day and felt her heart smile and said a small prayer, as she recalled how their relationships evolved from acquaintances to friends. It was something she was very grateful for.

2

The Homework Assignment

Claire

"Well, good morning! I got your text last night and have to say I'm a little anxious about what you're going to spring on me today," Claire said as Bryn approached the booth. "What's with this homework assignment stuff? I mean, I realize most people believe being a stay-at-home mom means I kill time shopping online in my yoga pants before picking up the kids from school, but I'm not really sure I have time for something like this."

Shaking her head, Bryn pulled out her laptop and sat down in the booth across from Claire. They were at their favorite breakfast diner, the place where they had been coming for years. Twice a week, they would drop their kids off at school and then rush to Maggie's to share coffee, gossip, and the special of the day. Claire and Bryn were friends from college, and, while not exactly close while they were in school, after discovering that their sons had the same teacher on the first day of kindergarten and that they lived less than a mile apart, they reconnected and set the stage for a best-friendship to blossom.

This morning's breakfast was different, however. Claire and Bryn had been talking for years at book clubs, play dates, birthday parties, and wine clubs (masked as bunco parties) about changing their lives. With their children (Claire has twin daughters and an older son, Bryn has a son and daughter) now in school full time, they were ready to do more. Both women had successful careers before deciding to leave the workforce to start families and were now ready to get back to work, become members of a professional organization, and feel the satisfaction of collecting a paycheck. Bryn was a lawyer, and Claire was a senior director at a technology consulting firm. Life with young children was full; managing schedules, sports activities, making sure the library books were returned on time, lunches packed, family vacations planned, laundry and grocery shopping completed, trying to keep the house from looking like something you don't have to apologize for, was tough. They loved their children and were grateful for the madness, but both wanted more.

"Daniel made the travel baseball team," Claire reported. "He's worked so hard on improving his batting and has actually been listening to his dad. He seems to appreciate that Evan knows what he's talking about since he played in college. Evan's reaction to the news was intense; you would have thought Daniel was a fifth-grade, first-round draft pick for the Cubs."

"That's awesome," Bryn shared, "But you know what this means, don't you?"

"Yep, I most certainly do," replied Claire. "Travel means time. We're talking away games and maybe overnight stays. With both girls in dance and after-school tutoring, I'm not sure how I'm going to keep up and figure out how to go back to work so I can have adult conversations again."

Bryn dove in, "That's why we're going to change our breakfast meetings starting today. Going forward, I think it would be cool to shift into work mode and treat our breakfasts as mini board meetings where we're the co-chairs of the board."

Claire was taking this in, "OK, a board of two? Or shall we invite the waiter, hostess, and Maggie, the owner, to join us as well? She does know how to run and market a successful business, not to mention, she makes a badass bacon waffle."

Bryn wasn't sure if Claire was taking her seriously. She had put a lot of thought into how to make their conversations around going back to work actionable and truly believed that to take the next step and turn their discussions into reality, they needed to start holding each other accountable. "Listen, Claire, I don't care who we invite, and to be honest, I think it would be pretty cool to grow this group and invite different perspectives into our conversations. For now, we launch this with just the two of us. Let's stop talking and do something, anything! Activity brings answers, and mulling breeds indecision. Let's go!"

Claire had so much respect for Bryn. They had talked about doing something that would get them on a path to go back to work, and now, Bryn was making this real. Her energy was contagious, and the more Claire thought about it, the more anxious she became. *Are we really going to do this?* Claire asked herself, shocked at how this idea was starting to scare her. *If I start this, Bryn will hold me accountable. Figuring out what I want to do and then putting myself out there to get rejected or judged sounds terrifying.*

"Earth to Claire; where'd you go, girlfriend?" Bryn asked.

The waiter approached, and the sound of the plate on the table snapped Claire back to the present. She stared down at her veggie omelet and thought, *Bryn's right, it's time to take action, but this all feels overwhelming.* Finally, Claire looked up and asked, "OK, so how do we start?"

Bryn had a huge smile on her face; she had feared Claire's commitment to this may waver. They had talked so often about re-igniting their careers, experiencing the thrill and satisfaction of doing a great job, contributing to a company's mission, and taking pride in bringing new ideas to the table and working with a team. They both had strong resumes and lists of accomplishments but had no idea where to start since they left their careers over five years ago. "OK, I know you well enough, and I know what you're thinking. We got this, Claire. We're smart, and we can help each other reconnect with the professional selves that we miss so much. Today represents our first board meeting, right here at this booth. It's just you and me, Claire, and this is as safe as it gets."

Claire waved for a refill of her coffee and said, "You're right, now tell me about this homework."

"You got it," Bryn said and started to stack the plates to make room for her computer. "Did you bring your laptop?" she asked.

"You were serious about that?" Claire responded as she pulled something from her tote. She realized she had forgotten her laptop when she pulled up to the diner, but the girls had left an old backpack in the back of the car, where Claire found something she could work with. "I have this," she said and smiled as she flashed the cover of the notebook, "I believe this is board room appropriate."

"Pink unicorns and My Little Pony stickers will definitely work," Bryn replied. "Ahhh, and let's not forget my rainbow gel ink pen," snickered Claire.

"OK, you know that after Matt and Katie go to bed, I dive into my stack of books and journals." Bryn began. "Charlie still thinks I'm a hoarder, but I don't care. Every professional subscription I overpay for makes me feel connected to my life before kids. Well, last week, I came across something that inspired me. I read this story about a guy that left his corner office to pursue his dream of being an author and speaker.

"I don't want to do either of those," Claire commented.

"For the love of God, Claire, let me finish. This guy talked about having a coach, and..." she felt she was losing Claire. "OK, I'll jump right to the punch line; he started this regular exercise with a coach type of person that mentored him. I don't know all of the details, but to kick off the coaching relationship, he was told to do a Homework Assignment."

"So that's where you got the idea from?" Claire asked.

"Yep! And here's how we get started." Bryn was proud of herself for bringing this idea to the table and was loaded with energy from sharing things and getting started with Claire. "OK, think about where you're at, right now, with your life, specifically your career goals and wanting to get back to work." Claire raised her eyebrows as her focus wandered off past the booth, and she sighed. "Now, fast forward twelve months from now and create a picture in your mind of where you want to be. Where are you working? Who are you working with? Even, what are you wearing? Get detailed, Claire, and then think about how it all makes you feel."

"Feel?!" Claire exclaimed. "How the hell am I supposed to know what I should be feeling twelve months from now?"

"I understand this may seem a bit ambiguous," Bryn replied. "Please hang in there with me...believe me, I thought the same thing when I read this guy's story, but here's the thing; if you can fast forward and think about having a goal and how living in that moment after you've achieved that goal makes you feel - well...Claire - I believe you can make that goal a reality. This mindset is the backbone of this guy's story, and it inspired me. It got me thinking about us and what our version of the Homework Assignment might look like. Will you try it with me?"

Claire really respected and loved Bryn. Bryn's passion and conviction regarding this exercise were infectious, and Claire was getting on board. She grabbed her gel pen, waved goodbye to the unicorn as she opened the notebook, and said, "Help me get started."

Bryn got comfy on her side of the booth, ready to set fire to her keyboard. She pulled up the PDF from a link in the story. Turning her laptop around, she tilted her screen so Claire could easily read the description of the exercise Bryn wanted her to complete. "OK, read through this, then begin your assignment by writing down 'twelve months from now, I, Claire Stanley, will be…'". Bryn paused then said, "Now finish the sentence." Claire looked at Bryn's screen and read through the outline.

THE HOMEWORK ASSIGNMENT

- Ground yourself; this is not a fleeting exercise and should not be rushed. It does not have to take hours (but it is perfectly fine if it does), but it does warrant planning quiet and quality time with yourself that is distraction-free.

- Take an inventory of where you are in your life right now with regards to your hopes, dreams, and goals. Ask yourself the question - What's great, what's not great, and what would you like to change?

- Now, fast forward in time. Consider twelve months to start. A year is a clear baseline and easy to process, but you can always push the timeline out, even layer timelines (twelve months, thirty-six months, five years - that might be long enough!)

- Next, you need to trust what comes to mind. No one needs to know your vision of the future but you (but there is power in sharing, see the last step). Just start writing - there is no wrong answer. Do you want to have an executive job, manage a team, travel the globe, be on the path to early retirement, have a great work/life balance? The sky is the limit because it's your goal and your dream. Write it all down, and don't care what it looks or sounds like.

- Then, take a pause and start thinking about how this vision makes you feel and write the feelings down. What kind of emotions are you experiencing? What feels natural? How does achieving your goals make you feel? What are the first things you start thinking about? Do you feel pride, relief, joy, satisfaction, hungry for more? Prioritize feeling positive.

- Once complete, take a break. Don't wait too long - but be sure to return to your entry to refine it where needed.

- Give thanks and channel gratitude for meeting your goal. Finish your assignment with closing line that starts with, "I am grateful for," and then, finish the sentence by describing all of the good in your life after having met your goal, including thanks for how you got there.

Claire looked up at Bryn after scrolling through the document. "OK, I get it. I just think I need some extra time to think about this."

"I totally understand; it's not as simple as it sounds, especially since the idea is brand new for you," Bryn replied.

"Anything else, ladies?" the two women heard Maggie ask.

"Nope, just the check, thank you," Claire replied as she reached for her credit card.

On the drive home, Claire was uneasy, anxious, and wondering if it was too early to tap the chardonnay she had opened the night before. *What did I think was going to happen?* she asked herself. *I mean, I've always believed in the power of positive thinking and always thought I took a glass-half-full approach to the world, and I want to set a good example for my kids, especially my daughters.* But Claire was uneasy, distracted, and sliding towards being disappointed in herself. As she continued her drive, she kept thinking about Bryn and how she glowed while she was tapping away on her laptop at the diner. Why wasn't she feeling that same energy? They started their homework assignments at the diner, but had she started hers wrong? She wrote three pages worth (well, doodled a bit at times) but felt so unaccomplished.

As she sat at a stop light, the sound of a horn snapped her out of her spiral, and she stepped on the gas only to bump into the car in front of her. She'd realized that the horn wasn't for her but for the person in the left turn lane that was ignoring the green arrow. "Dammit," she blasted and got out of her SUV. The bumper of the BMW in front of her was both scratched and dented. While there wasn't a significant amount of damage, this was destined to cost more than her insurance deductible. A man who looked like he had just walked off the golf course stepped out of the car, put his hands in his pockets, and examined his bumper. Claire guessed he was about twenty years older than her.

"You OK?" he asked Claire.

"Yes, fine - much better than your bumper," Claire replied. "I am extremely sorry, and I would like to try to take care of this without going through my insurance if possible. I'll give you my policy information in case I flake, but would prefer to pay for this repair myself."

The man took a closer look at the bumper and tried rubbing some of the scratches free with his finger. He stood up, turned to Claire, folded his arms, and nodded his head. "OK, let's exchange information, and I'll start by sending you the repair estimate first."

Claire felt a small wave of relief and extended her hand; however, her heart was still feeling like it could beat out of her chest. "Thank you, thank you so much for understanding, for being kind, for understanding, for..." she nervously babbled while shaking his hand.

"You're welcome, and don't worry. I have a feeling getting this fixed will not be an issue. I'm Max, Max Carlton," he said.

"Pleased to meet you, Max, well...I mean not this way - I'm Claire, Claire Stanley." As Claire reached into her purse to grab her insurance card, she could feel Max staring. When she looked up, she realized it was not at her but directly over her head.

"Claire?" Max asked, "Any relation?" Claire turned around and softly grinned. She couldn't go anywhere in town without the reminder of what her husband's smile looked like. The billboard on the other side of the road was for the local insurance agency with the name *Evan Stanley* in large print.

"Meet my husband, Evan," Claire said. They both chuckled, exchanged information, and Max went on his way.

That evening while Claire was making dinner, Evan walked in the door to see a glass of wine waiting for him on the island. "Hey, Bear," he said as he reached for the glass and walked over to give her a kiss. "Thank you for the vino; dinner smells great." Claire turned and smiled.

"You're welcome, and I rear-ended a BMW M5 on my way back from meeting Bryn at the diner today - I'd call the damage minor, plus."

"Well...OK...you seem alright; what about the guy driving the BMW?" Evan replied. Claire paused and processed Evan's response.

"You mean the person driving the BMW? Why would you assume it was a man?"

Evan looked up, puzzled, and responded, "How many women do you know that would drive an M5, Bear? Women fit more into the X5 SUV profile. I insure these things, I know."

Claire knew he was probably right but hated the stereotypes he subscribed to. Any other day, this wouldn't bother her, but today, she was frustrated and felt distracted and kept feeling like she had finished a homework assignment that was destined for a failing grade. She had such a hard time getting started at the diner. Sitting across the table from Bryn, watching her furiously type away, Claire couldn't help but feel intimidated. She wondered if she was truly ready to go back to work. She worried about why the Homework Assignment felt so daunting. Was it a sign? Should she wait for the twins to be older? Could she still be a good mother and wife if she went back to work? She recalled how she felt paralyzed by these questions, then thought, *the technology industry is so male-dominated; how do I integrate with a team of men that have not left the workforce and continued to develop their careers? Can I get the same type of position I had before I left? Level of responsibility? How do I start?*

Claire stood there, frozen, when she saw Evan jump up and open the oven. *Good God, that's what the beeping was in the background!* She thought to herself as she watched Evan turn off the timer.

"You sure you're OK, Claire? I can finish dinner if this accident thing has you shook up. We can talk more later."

Claire knew it wasn't the accident that was distracting her. Regardless, she was going to take Evan up on his offer.

"Thanks, that would be awesome," she replied and grabbed her tote, the rest of her wine, and walked upstairs to ponder what she should do next.

Walking into the bedroom, she was happy she had made the bed that day as she plopped on her back and stared at the ceiling. After some deep breathing and replaying the scene at the diner one more time in her mind, she sat up, propped some pillows, placed her glass of wine within arm's reach on the nightstand before pulling out her notebook. The unicorn brought a smile to her face as she opened to the first page and thought of the irony of her notebook.

In twelve months, I, Claire Stanley...

Gawd, this sounds like a last will and testament, Claire thought to herself. She crossed out the first sentence and wrote ...

*Claire Stanley, Vice President of Program Development,
(insert large consulting firm name here).*

OK, that feels better, she thought.

Claire loved the technical consulting world. The different people, places, and opportunities she was constantly introduced to were her favorite parts of the job. Claire loved moving into management, and she really enjoyed helping others define their own career paths. Consulting was in her blood, as her father retired from a large, global firm after thirty-five years of service. Her younger brother was also in the consulting world; as he made his march up the career ladder at the mid-sized firm he had interned with during college. Brian made his career climb seem simple and easy. He was the favorite, at least in Claire's mind he was. Her dad would bring both of them into the office, and when Brian would sit behind the large mahogany desk and spin in the chair until he got dizzy, their dad would say, "you're already on your path to partner, kiddo."

Claire continued to recall how she would muscle herself into the chair and use the lure of Tootsie Rolls in her dad's candy jar to distract her brother and get him to move. During one of their visits, Clare remembered bringing a notebook to her dad's office. She wanted to mirror what she saw him do when he left for work each morning. The last thing he would put into his briefcase was a leather-bound book. Once Claire took command of the chair that day, she pulled herself up to the desk and opened her notebook. She grabbed a pen from the cup on her dad's desk and started to write the alphabet Once she was done, she made a scribble at the bottom of the page to mimic the number of times she had watched her dad sign contracts at home. "Look, Daddy, I made my own work paper, just like yours. I'm going sit at a desk just like this when I grow up."

"OK, pumpkin," her dad replied. "Those desks are for boys; your desk is outside like the one Miss JoAnn sits at. You kid's ready to grab some ice cream?" Claire began to wonder just what kind of toll the bias toward her brother had taken on her over the years. She worked her way through school, landed academic scholarships for college, and then graduated with honors, while her brother went to school on a baseball scholarship, got grades good enough to ensure his eligibility to play, and spent his summer earnings before the end of the first semester each year.

As she thought about her younger brother's current path to senior partner, she wondered if returning to work would mean being surrounded by a team of Brians. *Geez, what would that be like? Will I be working for someone like my brother?* Claire sighed and closed the notebook. Mentally drained, she closed her eyes.

"Bears, honey? Are you hungry?" Evan was sitting next to Claire on the bed and gently rubbing her shoulder. Claire woke up ... the room was almost dark.

"What time is it? How long have I been sleeping?" Claire replied. She quickly sat up, knocking her notebook on the floor.

"What's this?" Evan asked as he picked the notebook up. Claire turned and sat on the side of the bed and took it from his hands.

"It's homework," she answered.

"What do the girls have going on?" Evan replied.

"It's not the girls' homework book; it's mine ... or at least, it's mine now." She cracked a small smile as she looked down at the book in her hands. After a big sigh, she looked over to Evan and could tell he was confused. "You know how Bryn and I have been talking about returning to work, especially now that our kids are in school full-time?" Evan leaned back on the bed and nodded. "Well, today at the diner, Bryn started to make things real. She read this interview about a guy that had self-published a book, and how he credits reaching this goal by starting to do this exercise he called a homework assignment." Claire went on to explain the process Bryn had walked her through, including capturing the details of what Claire's life could look like twelve months from now - back at work, and re-engaged with a team of people that focused on delivering consulting projects. Evan listened intently.

"So, is this a 'vision board' type of thing that you're doing?" he asked.

"Not exactly," Claire responded. "It's not just about setting a goal and describing a picture of what hitting that goal looks like, although visioning is part of it. It goes deeper into the details and includes things like how you'll feel once you've achieved your goal and being grateful for everything that's transpired. Make sense?"

Evan was trying to process what Claire was talking about. "So, did you get it done? What did you write? What do you want to do?" he asked.

"I feel like I wrote a bunch of stuff that doesn't mean anything, to be honest. You know, I really struggled with this and didn't know where to begin. Bryn and I have been talking about going back to work since the kids started school. It's always been easy for me to think about going back to consulting, but once I had to write down what that actually looked like, I froze. I sat across from Bryn, who had brought her laptop, and watched her type away and sprint to the end of her assignment and wondered, how was it so easy for her?"

"She's probably been thinking about it longer than you, Claire, and after having read that guy's story, she was just more prepared. That's all that was." Evan replied.

"Yeah...." she responded, "There was something else that came up for me. I felt really insecure and had a hard time thinking about the whole 'feeling' part. I started thinking about Brian and how he chose the same career path as me, and his success over the years, and how dad never questioned his career choices but often made me feel like I was making a mistake." Claire queued up her deepest voice and said, "Technical consulting can be a hard path for a woman to take, and you want to be a mother someday, don't you, Claire?" Claire ran her hand over the cover of the book. "You heard Dad last weekend, bragging about Brian; talking about how someday he'll be the CEO of his firm." Claire stood up, "Maybe I want to be CEO of a firm! Claire Stanley, CEO - I think that sounds freaking awesome!"

Evan sat up and grabbed Claire's hand. "Claire, you know I believe in you. It's your spirit and drive that first attracted me to you. Titles can be great but don't mean everything. And by the way, in case you needed reminding - you already have the title of CEO."

Claire looked confused, "What are you talking about?"

"Claire, you're the CEO of this family!" Claire's eyes squinted as she processed what Evan had just said. "Um.... that's well... one way to look at my role as a wife and mother. It is one of the toughest yet satisfying jobs I've ever had in my life. You know, there are some pretty incredible time management and executive decision making skills I've developed over the years. It's too bad you can't put that on a resume and be taken seriously." She paused. "Thank you for saying that, Evan. Now, I think we should probably go check on the kids."

Evan popped off the bed and said, "I'm on it, ma'am," and went downstairs.

Claire turned on the light and sat back down on the bed. *Was he serious? Did he listen? Did he really think that comment would make me feel better?* Claire was now more frustrated than ever. She set the notebook on the edge of the nightstand and headed downstairs and join the rest of the family.

That night, Claire couldn't sleep. She was tossing and turning and replaying conversations with her family and friends, starting from back in college to earlier that night with Evan. Why did she always feel like she had to prove herself? Why did she feel like she had to do twice as well as her younger brother to get half the recognition that he received? Was it the way they were brought up? Was it the male-dominated industry she had chosen? *I have to master this; I want to figure this out*, she thought, then decided to get out of bed. She grabbed her notebook and went downstairs to start some coffee.

Sitting down at the kitchen table, she opened the unicorn cover to a blank page and wrote, Claire Stanley, CEO of Sterns Warner. "Why not?" she said to herself as she took a sip of coffee and continued to write.

As CEO of Sterns Warner, Claire is responsible for the development and execution of Sterns Warner's operations and business strategies and oversees organizational decisions to ensure they are in alignment with the company's objectives. Claire was a managing director prior to her leaving the organization to start a family and returned to the company in the same role, after which she developed a global practice and was promoted to SVP of Operations.

"Hmmm - that actually feels good," Claire said to herself. "OK, keep going - now how did you get there?

She returned to Sterns Warner as a managing director, responsible for a regional team that incubates technical solution offerings for the company to deliver.

Claire knew there were some gaps she had to address with regard to her technical training. It was impossible for her to keep up with the latest tech trends between PTO meetings and carpools. "Forget that Claire; don't get distracted. You're smart and ready, and Bryn says there's no wrong answer."

Role details:

- *I am managing a small team.*
- *We're developing new solutions to take to market every quarter.*
- *I am able to work from home two days a week.*
- *I am part of an executive leadership program intended to advance managing directors' careers.*
- *I have direct access to the company's executive leadership team.*
- *My boss is supportive and collaborates with me often.*
- *I go to work every day feeling confident.*
- *I work in an environment where I can take risks.*
- *My team's solutions are helping to land some of the company's top customers.*

- *My practice is profitable.*
- *I am being paid higher than the industry average and have good benefits.*

Claire sat back and looked at the page. *I can see it; I can actually begin to feel what this would be like,* she thought to herself. *How much more do I write? Is there a minimum amount of words? How much did Bryn write? OK, OK - stop thinking too much and get to that feel part, now.*

How Does This Make Me Feel?

Landing a job that would put me back in management and on a path to becoming CEO:

- *Validated. I am connecting people and our organization to new ideas and solution offerings.*
- *Authoritative.*
- *Smart and intelligent.*
- *Recognized for ability to lead and make others successful.*
- *Empowered to drive more of my own thinking.*
- *Proud that I'm generating an income.*
- *Happy that I'm setting a good example for my girls*

(then Claire paused and stopped), *no, for my children! Daniel needs to see women experiencing professional success as well!*

- *Happy that I'm setting a good example for my ~~girls~~ family*
- *Satisfied about setting and achieving a goal.*

Claire put her pen down and re-read her entry. She

smiled, then giggled a little as she could not believe how good it felt to envision the future, her future. Going back to work and getting back on track to meet (*no ... master!*) her professional goals, now seemed like a real possibility. In the next moment Claire's feelings went from glee to worry. *How do I get started? I don't even have a resume! How do I explain what I've been doing for the past eleven years of my life?* She ran her hand over the page in her notebook and thought about sitting behind her dad's mahogany desk. *He's wrong*, she thought to herself. *I do belong behind that desk.*

Bryn

"Conner, Alexis! Let's go; you're going to be late!" Bryn shouted from the kitchen as she was packing lunches and lining up book bags. "Conner, your shirt's on backwards," Bryn commented as she watched her son walk into the kitchen. Bryn's oldest son Conner shrugged his shoulders and sat down in front of his bowl of cereal. "Alexis, why are you still in your PJs?" she asked as her daughter shuffled herself over to the table, sat down grabbed her spoon.

"They have bunnies on them, Mommy," Alexis replied.

"I can see that, dear, but that doesn't explain why you're still wearing them when we're about to leave for school," Bryn said as she packed up her laptop and prepared for her day.

"Because they match my slippers," Alexis answered. Bryn paused. As a corporate lawyer at Tabor International, she had managed complex acquisitions and negotiated some of the company's largest contracts but was struggling with this seven-year-old's case regarding why she was still in her PJs. "This is what I'm wearing to school today. I brushed my teeth and I think I look nice, and this is what I want to wear."

Bryn looked at Conner, "Makes my backward shirt less of a big deal now, doesn't it?' He said smugly.

"OK, kids, here's the deal; we have ten minutes and plenty left to do. Alexis, pajamas are not appropriate to wear outside of the house. Yes, you look nice, but that doesn't make it OK to wear them to school. Please go change. Conner..."

"Already on it, Mom," he replied as he turned his shirt around.

Once in the car and on their way to school, Bryn ran through the agenda for the day. "I need you both to hustle to the car when school lets out today, Conner has a dentist appointment, and the new office is farther away from school. I don't want to be late. Then Cali is coming over tonight to watch you guys because Daddy and I have an event to go to."

"What kind of event?" Alexis asked.

"It's a charity event; think of it as a party to raise money for a women's shelter," Bryn replied.

"Why is the shelter just for women?" Alexis innocently asked.

"That's a great question, sweetheart. This place is a special home where women and their children and even their pets can go when they are in trouble and have nowhere else to live." Bryn looked in the review mirror and could see Alexis processing her response. "The party your dad and I are going to tonight is going to raise money to help pay for this place where women can stay and get help and training until they can afford to live on their own."

Alexis was still pondering. "When's Daddy coming home?" she asked.

"He should be home by the time we get back from the dentist," Bryn replied. Charlie had been gone all week, and Bryn was ready for his return. As a commercial real estate agent Charlie had worked his way up to the senior vice president and was now responsible for the entire US with more than a hundred brokers reporting to him. With his eye on a North American position, he had to commit to a heavy travel schedule and was gone almost half of the time. "OK, kiddos, I love you. Have a great day and remember to hustle here after school."

Bryn watched Conner and Alexis walk into school and smiled. She felt blessed and gave thanks for having two healthy children. Her life was good; she was happily married and had a nice home she enjoyed sharing with friends and family. Her kids were healthy, and they loved school. Life was good, but she was still missing something. As she put the car into drive and headed towards the diner, she smiled to herself and thought, *Today's the day I take that first step. I'm not sure how to do this, but I'm ready to try.*

Bryn arrived at the diner and started looking for Claire but could not find her. *Hmm, I thought I was going to be late*, she thought to herself. "Hiya, sweetheart!" she heard from the other side of the diner.

"Hey, Maggie! Have you seen Claire?"

"No Claire, but I got a spot for you right here with coffee on the way!"

Bryn replied, "Thanks, Mags," and slid into the booth to get comfortable. She took out her laptop and pulled up her homework assignment.

Corporate Transaction Attorney, Bryn Miles

Manages sophisticated M&A, private equity, and general corporate matters for Tabor's Fortune 500 companies. With a team of research specialists and associates reporting to her, Bryn ensures that the company's transactions comply with state laws and regulations to avoid legal risks and violations. Having negotiated one of the largest acquisitions in her company's history, Bryn has returned to Tabor International after a leave of absence to assume a senior role on the M&A team. A member of various advisory boards, Bryn assists with the development of company policy and consults on corporate legal processes.

Details:

- Represent the company in legal proceedings (administrative boards, court trials etc.).
- Work in a progressive and diverse environment.
- Manage major acquisitions and sit on the company's executive board.
- Report directly to the company's Chief Legal Officer.
- Flexible schedule and reasonable billable hour requirement, with the opportunity to work from home.
- Competitive compensation plan with generous vacation policy.
- Continuing education opportunity.
- Engagement with a corporate social responsibility initiative.
- Supportive management.

- Work with a competent team and have the autonomy to manage freely.
- Ability to work on global projects.

How Does This Make Me Feel?:

- Empowered because I'm in a position to work with a team and make a difference.
- Curious and driven as I can use my experience and expertise again.
- Accomplished as I set a goal to re-enter corporate law and did it.
- Energized from doing good work and getting projects completed on time.
- Supported by my co-workers, who understand my family life and respect my need for work/life balance.
- Loved by my family, who respect the fact that I have gone back to work without them feeling compromised.
- Scared because I know there are more opportunities for me to grow and make a difference, and I don't know what this means.

"Excuse me, is this the board meeting for moms going back to work and ready to kick ass?" Bryn looked up and was a bit startled as she was deep in the review of her homework assignment.

"It is, but only if you're ready!" she smiled and replied. Claire sat down and settled into the booth.

"Here you are, my dear," Maggie said as she poured her friends' coffee and handed out the menus. "Something new today on the menu, ladies, homemade Greek yogurt with honey, fruit, and granola with your choice of toast, whatcha think?"

Both Claire and Bryn nodded and smiled with their eyes wide open like it was Christmas morning. "We'll take two, please," they said at the same time.

"OK, be right back!" Maggie replied and shuffled off to the kitchen.

"So where do we start, my friend?" Claire asked. "I have to admit; this exercise was a bit more difficult, well...maybe more terrifying than I thought it was going to be. I mean, last time we left the diner after teeing this whole thing up, I was consumed. You and I have been talking about going back to work for so long. When we've talked over breakfast or glasses of wine, everything always seemed easy and clear and..." Claire paused as she searched for her next word.

"It didn't get real until we put pen to paper - right?" Bryn replied. "I totally understand, and I was thinking about you and how the whole thing had been top-of-mind for me days before we met, so I had already worked through some of the anxiety because I had a head start on you. I can't wait to see what you wrote." Claire moved the place setting to make room for her yogurt as she pulled out her notebook. "Sticking with the unicorn, I see?" Bryn chuckled.

"Well, I've upgraded to blue ink, and I absolutely love the irony of capturing something that I want to make real in this thing. I'm kind of attached to it now."

Bryn smiled, "OK, I didn't mean to send us on a tangent - whatcha got?"

Claire turned the page and handed her notebook over to Bryn. As she watched her hold the notebook, Claire could feel her heart beating and wondered if she was going to break into a sweat. Bryn was one of her best friends, someone who never judged her, so why was she so nervous? "Vulnerability does that to you, I suppose." Claire blurted.

Bryn looked up, "What?" Claire realized that her thoughts had just made themselves public at the table.

"Sorry, that was involuntary. I didn't realize I was thinking out loud," she replied.

Bryn put the notebook down and smiled. "This is really awesome, Claire, so you think you want to go back to Sterns after all. You've often talked about the environment and lack of female leadership and your frustrations around not being taken seriously because you're a woman. I realize technology is a male-dominated environment, much like law, but do you think you should consider looking at other companies?"

Claire took her last bite of yogurt and looked up at Bryn. "That thought never crossed my mind. I'm actually a bit embarrassed that I didn't think about that. It just seemed obvious that I would return to Sterns. I mean, Gordon's still there and told me to let him know if I ever wanted to come back." Claire started to feel overwhelmed again. *Sterns Warner was not the ideal work environment, but then did one exist?* The numerous times Gordon would take her male peers out after work and not invite her did wear her patience. His references to "when Claire would start a family" made her feel like she stuck out for the wrong reasons.

"Men start families too; why doesn't anyone talk about how their careers will change?" Claire blurted for the second time.

"More thinking out loud?" Bryn asked.

"Sorry, you're right; it's a really excellent point and one that I need to think about more."

Bryn was quick to respond, "Listen, I'm not here to discount anything you wrote down. This is really thoughtful, especially the part about you being a CEO. That's new and was very awesome to read."

Claire pushed her bowl aside and leaned on the table toward Bryn. "You know what Evan said to me last night?" Bryn shook her head no. "He said that I was the CEO of our family. My initial reaction was WTF, but then I thought about it more. Think about all of the decision making, planning and honestly leadership we bring to our families every day. Isn't it sad that we can't capture that on a resume and be taken seriously?"

Bryn agreed. "We really should get business cards made up. Family CEO and person responsible for turning young humans into honest, societal contributors." The women laughed as they drank their coffee. Bryn smiled and said, "I know your initial reaction was WTF, but you know he was just trying to help."

"I know, at first I thought it made him sound completely out of touch" Claire replied. "I know he's supportive and is on board with me going back to work, but when I initially heard him describe me that way, it made me feel like I had done something wrong to make him forget about what type of professional I was when I met him."

"Do you not like hearing that because you fear that's how you also view yourself?" Bryn responded. "Obviously, the reminder that your professional status had changed struck a nerve, and that's OK. Just think about why it bothered you so much, Claire, then think about how you'd like to change it."

"You really should have majored in psych," Claire replied. "I appreciate your feedback and feel better about working on my next version of this. But now it's your turn - hand it over. It's time you dove into Maggie's yogurt." Bryn turned her laptop around and slid it across the table.

Claire took a few minutes to read what Bryn had captured. "Dang girl, this is solid. Clean, direct, really well-written. You know what my favorite part of your assignment is, Bryn?" Bryn shook her head while she enjoyed another spoonful of yogurt. "The very last bullet. The line where you lead with the word, 'scared.' That's a brave statement to make and I'm curious, what made you add that in?"

Bryn set down her spoon and looked up at Claire. "You know, I took it out and put it back in several times. It haunted me while I was working on finishing this thing. I felt like if I didn't include that bullet, then the whole thing would be a farce. I want to go back to work, I have the support of my husband, but I'm worried about the impact on my family. I know that I want and need to do this."

Claire pulled the laptop closer and read the bullet out loud, "Scared because I know there are more opportunities for me to grow and make a difference, and I don't know what that means." Claire reached out and grabbed Bryn's hand. "We got this, Bryn; let's be scared together."

They left the diner and walked through the parking lot. They were stopped by a speeding car. "Christ! What makes people think it's OK to go sixty in a parking lot!" Bryn angrily said. Claire looked at the car and saw it was a black BMW M5.

"Would you ever drive that car?" she asked Bryn.

"I don't know; I can't imagine what it would be like to drive something that didn't have third-row seating. Maybe someday. Why do you ask?" Claire shrugged her shoulders.

"No real reason - just curious." The friends hugged and congratulated each other on another successful board meeting.

"OK, next week, final versions of our assignments, and then we work on our plans," Bryn said. Claire gave her a thumbs up before getting into her car.

Bryn was mindful of her time as she had a few errands to run before getting the kids from school. The next stop would be the mall, where she would pick up her dress for the charity gala before crossing off the remainder of her to-do list. As she pulled out of the parking lot, she kept replaying the conversation about being scared. It wasn't the homework assignment itself that she struggled with; she had been excited about doing it from the first time she heard about it. It was how she felt now that it was done. Bryn was hoping for clarity and confidence around having outlined her professional future, but that's not what she felt. The job description and responsibilities she wrote about were all things she knew she wanted. So why did she still feel like something was lacking?

Walking through the mall and entering the department store, she decided to take a break from her thoughts around the homework assignment and focus on the evening she and Charlie had planned. "Can I help you?" an older and sharply dressed woman asked Bryn as she walked up to the counter in the dress department.

"Yes, hello - my name is Bryn Miles, and I'm here to pickup a gown that was being altered."

"Certainly, one moment, please - would you like to try it on one more time?" Bryn looked at her watch and was ahead of schedule.

"Sure, thank you," she replied and followed the woman into the dressing room. After a few minutes, the woman walked in with Bryn's gown. It was prettier than she had remembered it, and she grew more excited about having a real, grown-up, night out with Charlie.

"It's just gorgeous," the woman said as she helped Bryn zip up the back. Bryn stepped onto a platform in front of the mirror and was in love. The strapless, black satin dress was simple and elegant. She couldn't wait for Charlie to see her in it. "Are you going to a wedding?" the woman asked.

"No, my husband and I are going to a black-tie charity event this evening," Bryn replied. "It's a fundraiser for the Campbell House women's shelter." The woman took a step back and put her head down for a moment. Bryn turned around and could tell that the woman's mind had slipped somewhere else. "Are you OK?" Bryn asked.

The woman looked up, and Bryn could see the tears in her eyes. "That is a very special place with very special people that saved my life," the woman shared.

Bryn didn't know what to say. It was hard to imagine that this woman had ever struggled so deeply that she turned to a women's shelter. "I would love to hear your story; if you don't mind talking about, it that is."

The woman smiled and nodded and proceeded to tell Bryn about her husband passing away and the point where she discovered how financially destitute they were. "I had no idea how much money we owed. We had no savings, and with no children or family; once I got evicted from our apartment, I had nowhere to go." Bryn reached out and held the woman's hand as she continued to describe the first time she slept in a park and how she and others would wait in the alley behind certain restaurants, hoping for handouts when employees would step outside for smoke breaks. One night, while she waited alone for a diner's back door to open, she was greeted by a woman from the restaurant with a bag filled with take-out containers and a piece of paper. "She handed me a shopping bag of food and asked me to go to the address on the paper. She told me to ask for Colleen and that I would be able to spend the night there. That address was the Campbell House shelter." Bryn felt the goosebumps spill over her body.

"I met Colleen, and she found me a bed in the shelter for a few days. She was a counselor and asked me all kinds of questions about my past. She was so kind and easy to talk to. I told her stories about how my mother taught me to sew and how I used to make clothes. She found a woman's home for me to live in and even brought me a sewing machine and fabrics. I got my confidence back and realized that I could still sew well. She then helped me look for jobs, and that's how I ended up working here. I love what I do now, and it all started with the wonderful people at Campbell House."

Bryn was floored. She could not remember a time when she had felt so sympathetic, amazed, and inspired. "Thank you, thank you so much for sharing your story," Bryn replied. "You were so strong and brave and, wow, such an inspiration. And I'm so sorry - I don't even know your name."

"I'm Gloria, Gloria Meyers," the woman replied and stuck out her hand.

"Thank you for making my day, Gloria, with your beautiful story," Bryn said and knew it would be safe to give her a hug.

Back at the department store counter, Bryn watched Gloria wrap up her dress as if it were a piece of fine china. You could tell she really took pride in her work, and Bryn was so happy to know that she had now landed on her feet and was supporting herself. Gloria handed the dress bag to Bryn and said, "I'm delighted to know that there will be people like you at the event tonight that are there to help others." Bryn nodded and thanked Gloria again for her time, but as she left the store, Gloria's parting sentence made her wonder. *Am I attending this event to truly help others, or was it a way to get quality time with Charlie and enjoy a nice night out?*

Later that evening, Bryn was making some final adjustments to her hair and makeup when she heard Charlie shout, "Honey, the car is here!" Bryn walked down the stairs and was greeted by her smiling family. "Mommy, you look like a princess," said her daughter.

"Sweetheart, you're stunning," said Charlie as he grabbed her hand and led her out the door. Bryn was walking on a cloud as her family's comments made her heart melt. Charlie opened the door, and as Bryn stepped into the limo, she saw the champagne. *He really does think of everything* she thought as Charlie stepped into the car from the other side. Before they had left the driveway, Charlie had popped the champagne and was preparing to toast. "To my beautiful wife and all that she does for our family. I know my travel schedule has been tough, and you're doing an amazing job at home. I look forward to giving you a great night off." Bryn smiled and took a sip.

"OK, my turn," she replied. "To you and us and our family and to Gloria!" Charlie looked baffled and asked who Gloria was. Bryn flashed a big smile and almost giggled as she was so excited to tell Charlie the amazing story of the woman who had helped her at the department store.

As the car pulled up to the charity venue, Bryn was still talking about the impression this woman made on her and how her story had lifted her up - engrossed in everything she was feeling, she didn't realize they had arrived. "Honey, we're here - it's time to get out," whispered Charlie.

"Oh! Right! Let's go!" Bryn said as the driver opened the car door. They walked down the red carpet and stopped to pose for pictures along the way.

Charlie held Bryn's hand and leaned in to say, "before I forget, I loved your story about Gloria. It's spectacular that you met her today and that she had a connection to the event we're attending right now. You know what they say?"

Bryn whispered back, "There's no such thing as coincidence."

Once inside, Bryn was drinking in the beauty of the venue and how it had been decorated. There were banners everywhere representing the people that had walked the halls of The Campbell House shelter and had successfully graduated and were now happily on their own. Each banner told the story of a person that had been given the gift of empowerment to change their lives with the support of the shelter. Bryn was really moved and felt a personal attachment to each person she read about as Gloria was with her in spirit the entire time.

"Bryn, honey – I'd like you to meet someone," Bryn heard Charlie say, which caused her to stop and turn around. "This is Max Carlton; he's the president of the board for Campbell House."

"Nice to meet you, Max, I must say that this event is impressive, and the mission and impact of the shelter are incredible. I've really enjoyed walking around the room and reading the success stories of the people whose lives have been wonderfully touched by what you do."

Max shook Bryn's hand. "Thank you for saying that, Bryn; that means a lot. There is a great deal to celebrate, but there is still so much more to do. Our goal tonight is to inspire everyone to share their resources with our organization through the stories that we're telling, but the reality is that the problems that plague the women we serve are building, and we're doing our very best to keep providing them with assistance." Bryn's heart was breaking. The thought of Gloria not being able to get the support she so desperately needed was upsetting.

Max continued, "There are so many behind-the-scenes resources and expenses that people don't realize are required to provide good programming. Take legal coverage for example, we have compounding issues around the care of the children that come to the center as there's no precedent or policy regarding child protective services. Who wants to separate a child from their family? We most certainly do not but find ourselves constantly combating legislation that feels like it's in direct opposition to our mission. We can't afford experienced legal resources to keep up."

Bryn felt her heart beating and her eyes getting misty. Every ounce of Max's speech was connecting to her soul. Her brain started to fire on all cylinders about how to proactively prepare to combat legislation that was going to challenge the shelter, in addition to new ideas that could actually impact the future of the residents.

Her thought process was interrupted by a woman walking up to their group and apologizing but she clearly needed to give Max the hook so they could start the first round of presentations for the evening. "Excuse me, I'm sorry to interrupt, but Max is needed backstage as we're getting ready to kick off our presentations," said the young woman, now standing next to Max.

"Charlie and Bryn, it's my pleasure to introduce you to Colleen Warner, Director of Social Services at Campbell House." While Max's introduction was simple, Bryn was now overwhelmed with a sea of emotions as she realized that this was "the Colleen" that helped change Gloria's life.

"It's a pleasure to meet you, Colleen; actually, what makes this introduction even more interesting is that we have a common friend." Bryn was a little surprised that she just categorized Gloria as a friend.

"Nice to meet you, and who is our friend?" Colleen asked. Bryn told the story about picking up her dress that day, and everyone was in awe. "Gloria is one of my favorite cases. She is smart, creative, and has an enormous heart. I'm just tickled that you crossed paths with her and that she was brave enough to share her story." beamed Colleen.

"Max, we have to get your mic up and ready to kick things off. My apologies, but we need to head backstage." Charlie and Bryn completely understood and shook hands one last time before heading to their table. Bryn's head was spinning.

The evening was a hit, and the shelter exceeded its financial goals between ticket sales, raffles, and silent auctions. As Charlie and Bryn rode home, Bryn had her head on Charlie's shoulder as they relaxed in the back of the limo. "Hey, how is Claire doing? Weren't you two going to share plans for going back to work or something?" Charlie asked.

"She's great, and our planning has taken off, sorry babe - I'm just a little tired right now, but I appreciate you asking." Bryn wasn't tired at all but consumed with how she was going to re-write her entire homework assignment the next day.

3

The Accountability Log

Colleen

The smell of fresh coffee and cooking bacon woke Colleen up. The sun was peeking through the blinds, which made her smile. She rolled out of bed and thought about the success of the evening before and how well the charity event went. Stepping out of bed, grabbed her robe, and almost skipped into the kitchen. She was so excited to tell Meg about everything that happened the night before.

"Hey, you! Good morning! I thought I'd let you sleep in a bit since I know you had a late night," Meg said as she turned away from the stove to greet Colleen.

"Oh my God—breakfast smells amazing. As if my last twenty-four hours could not get better, my wife is preparing a breakfast feast that includes my favorite foods and, wait – are those your famous banana bread muffins?!" Colleen replied.

Meg and Colleen had been married for almost two years after a long courtship that started at a mutual friend's birthday party. Colleen had worked as the Director of Social

Services at Campbell House for almost four years but had a seven-year tenure there as she started out as a Project Manager and worked her way up the ladder. She and Meg instantly connected as Meg was an RN and was part of a volunteer organization that provided free healthcare to the homeless. Their shared passion for helping others and giving freely of their time and resources was something their friends and family admired and celebrated about them.

"Listen, I know you understand, but I am still sorry that I couldn't make it last night and share your awesome evening. I appreciate you sending the texts and pictures. You looked amazing. I've been dying for you to wake up so I can hear more," Meg said as she placed a beautifully plated slice of quiche, some bacon, and an aromatic muffin in front of Colleen.

"Yes, it was awesome, and again thank you for breakfast. But more importantly, how is Betts?" Meg's mom was dying of stage four lung cancer and was in hospice care. Just prior to the charity event, she took a turn for the worse, and all of her caregivers (Meg included) believed that it was just a matter of days before she might take her last breath. Meg was going to be by her side as much as she could be.

"Mom's OK, she actually had a better night than we had expected. She was alert, and we held hands a lot as she floated in and out of naps. She seemed very peaceful." Meg replied. "But I really want to focus on you and all of the positive things that happened last night. I could use the distraction."

"You got it!" Colleen shouted as she set down her coffee

mug. "Take a seat; I have plenty to share." Colleen went on to talk about the energy of the event and the amount of money they had raised. "And the best part," she added. "Wasn't even the financial success, but the number of people that signed up to volunteer at the shelter."

"That's really awesome, Col, and something you didn't even include in last week's AL!" AL stood for Accountability Log and was a coaching and mentoring exercise that started when Meg was on a six-month mission trip to Haiti. The girls had been dating for a few months and were looking for a way to stay connected since Meg was going to be living somewhere that had limited cellular and internet access. Because they were so like-minded and wired for caregiving, the two found it easy to connect on their goals and dreams every time they were together. Whether over a glass of wine after work or tea and coffee in the morning, the energy they felt and the trust they built around coaching and mentoring each other was tremendous. Each of their coaching sessions started with reflecting on their previous week's activities and lessons learned. They would then talk about new goals for the upcoming week and would describe what they wanted to accomplish. What started out as a casual conversation at the end of each week turned into something truly meaningful that served as a type of North Star for the girls, helping them prioritize and focus on goals they wanted to tackle next.

"Megs, this quiche is outstanding; did you use a new recipe?" Collen asked.

"Yeah, I came across a huge stack of cooking magazines when I was cleaning up during one of Mom's naps. I made a few changes and am so glad you like it," Meg replied as she picked up Colleen's plate.

"You really need to share this one with my mom for her menu at the diner; I know she was looking to change things up a bit. Listen, I most likely won't be home this afternoon as I'm going to the office to do some prep work for my Monday staff meeting. I've been thinking about sharing the concept of AL with the team as a way to build more trust between everyone and provide them with a way to coach and mentor each other. We have no money for outside training of any type, so I'm trying to get creative and offer them something that they can personally and professionally develop on a shoestring budget."

Meg turned around and flipped a dishtowel onto her shoulder, "So, would you have your staff recap the Physical and Career categories too, or just have them focus on Professional?"

Colleen stood up to refill her coffee, "All of it! Why not? We are dealing with the stress of trying to manage our client's future every day, and that extends beyond helping them find a job. Being able to share my intentions each week around staying physically and mentally strong is important. The exercise has changed my life, and I believe you can say the same. My staff is the hardest working team I have ever been a part of, and I want to do something to help them grow."

Meg walked over to Colleen and put her hands on her shoulders, "I think it's a beautiful idea; I never thought about how AL could actually apply in the workplace. You're right, as usual; by the way, your staff is lucky to have you. So, now what? How do you start introducing our magic concept to a group of people?"

Colleen shrugged her shoulders and giggled a bit, "I have no idea. I was thinking about heading into the office today to outline a few things, maybe create some worksheets, and lay everything out on our whiteboard. I'm really not sure, but what I do know is that this feels right, and you know what I say about activity brings answers!"

Meg smiled, "I can't wait to hear how this works out, and the timing of today is good as well because I'm going to head over to spend some time with Mom until Louie shows up."

"Sounds like a plan; let's find a happy hour somewhere and do our own AL review when we're done. I'm gonna jump in the shower and get to the office and do something with this idea. Give your brother a big hug for me, OK?" replied Colleen as she headed up the stairs and flashed the sign language sign for "I love you" with her right hand to Meg who was still standing in the kitchen.

Meg smiled and returned the sentiment and thought, *Colleen is really onto something.*

The Campbell House offices were two blocks away from the actual shelter. Since Colleen took over as director, she was able to manage her budget and double the number of staff that helped run the operation, resulting in them outgrowing their small office space that was on the third floor of the shelter. Max Carlton was the chairman of the board and had donated the space; the building was one of the many commercial properties he managed. Colleen now had eight full-time employees that complimented a few part-time folks and a sea of volunteers. Driving to the office, she felt even more inspired than she had over breakfast about introducing the concept of AL to her team. She could feel her confidence grow when she drove past the shelter and toward their new office space. She thought about the power of setting goals and trusted her coaching sessions with Meg. She loved tying it all to the power of manifestation, which was something she deeply believed in.

As she unlocked the office door and walked towards her desk, she turned to look at the poster of Gandhi she had brought to the office that had one of her favorite quotes:

"Your beliefs become your thoughts, your thoughts become your words, Your words become your actions, Your actions become your habits, Your habits become your values, Your values become your destiny."

And AL is how we can sort and manage this, she thought to herself. She walked over to the poster, reached up, and placed her hand on the words. "Amen," she said out loud and started to remember the very first Accountability Log she and Meg had shared after Meg left for Haiti. *There's real power in this exercise; I know it, and I know it will help my team*, she thought. *The focus, collaboration, and feedback is invaluable; I know this is going to work.*

She turned and walked toward her desk, where she placed her backpack, slid out her laptop and water bottle, then walked toward the conference room door. After lining up the dry-erase markers on the long wooden table, she slowly reached for her favorite color and, in purple, wrote on the board: The Accountability Log. She briefly outlined the three areas she and Meg tracked each week, then thought, *I really should type this up.* She pulled a chair over to where her laptop sat and started typing.

THE ACCOUNTABILITY LOG

Purpose - A platform that supports both personal and professional development. By recording weekly goals for key aspects of your life, the Accountability Log allows you to capture and measure your progress regarding having met each goal, in addition to capturing key observations and lessons learned for the week. Success is achieved by sharing these details with an Accountability Log partner that will provide feedback and coaching on a weekly basis. The goal is to dream big, organize your next steps, and manifest what you desire.

- Personal – This is about your mental and physical health. Capture the activity you did the previous week (exercise, diet, meditation, etc.), then set new goals for the following week as you look forward.

- Professional – This focuses on your current job/profession and what you want to accomplish. This is your day job/the one that pays the bills. Capture your goals and intentions and celebrate your successes. Identify what you want to change or update for the next week and use what you write as your guide.

- Career – This describes your long-term goals and dreams about the type of work you aspire to do as you think of the next chapter of your life and your future. This may or may not be tied to what you capture in Professional. How do you want to live, and what do you want to be doing? This can be as near term as the next twelve months or far out through retirement.

Format - Once you identify an Accountability Log partner, at the end of each week, reflect and document what you did in each category. Then think about the upcoming week and capture what you want to accomplish. This can include setting new goals or sticking to whatever is working for you. There is no wrong answer. When your log for the week is completed, schedule a time with your Accountability Log partner and review your entries.

Result - Evaluation of your priorities, reflective learning, and strong collaboration from a trusted partner will help you create great new habits and achieve your goals.

Colleen paused and stared at the screen. She thought about what her long-term goals were. She looked around the conference room, then down at the watermarked table that displayed the rings of coffee mugs from meetings held by previous tenants. The office wasn't fancy, but it was comfortable - and accommodating for their growth. Colleen wanted to provide a good work environment for her team, a place where people enjoyed showing up and were comfortable, but she just didn't have the budget to do everything. She loved the mission of the shelter and knew they were doing amazing things, but she still had a longing to create something on her own. She thought about the years she and Meg had used the AL process, which continued even after Meg's return from Haiti. A few mouse clicks later, she found herself in their very first Accountability Log Google Doc. She scrolled until she found what she was looking for.

=== 26 June ===

(Colleen) - Excited about finding a way to continue our weekly coaching sessions while you're in Haiti. Last week was tough; I found myself feeling a little lost without my coach and partner to connect with, but I'm already feeling more focused. I believe this virtual platform will work.

Personal – I'm actually eating better (well, maybe less because I'm lacking access to your delicious cooking) but have not gone to the gym in over a week. I know I need to start that again because it also contributes to my mental health and overall feeling of wellness. I think I am going to try meditation again; my focus has been off, and I know it will only help me. Overall, I have not been giving myself the mental or physical attention I need, which only I can change.

- *Looking forward* – Set some easy goals to meet, which include going to the gym three times and practicing meditation for ten minutes a day to start. I'm going to stay positive about the amazing things you are doing in Haiti to make sure I don't sad-sack over too many glasses of wine.

Professional – Work continues to go well, and we received a generous and anonymous donation last week. The kitchen can now get some much-needed improvements, which is a project I have been put in charge of. The biggest issue continues to be the complete lack of resources vs. the number of people who are in need each week. I am one of a team of four, and we could easily double our team and still need more people. I've been at the shelter for almost three years and long for a change, some days. I still believe I could do the job of director, but I need to wait for that opportunity to open up. In the meantime, I'll continue to build my network and connect with our board members.

- *Looking forward* - I'm going to start a weekly activity report for the board that details everything our team has accomplished for the week, and that highlights where we still have gaps. I think something short and simple will provide value as the board will receive operational details on a weekly basis while I keep the commercial running about our extended resources and increasing demands.

Career – I continue to look around me and mentally enter my dream world of "I'm my own non-profit and have unlimited resources." One of the things that keeps me in my current job is the fact that it's a great training ground for me for my role as CEO when I have my own gig someday. The network I'm building is strong. Just last week, I was introduced to a community that helps women re-enter the workforce, and I brainstormed with their leadership about how each of our clients could benefit from meeting each other and starting a mentorship program. The energy I felt after that conversation was incredible, and I'm convinced that I'm on to something.

- *Looking forward* – This week, I'm going to start an idea checklist to make sure I capture each new thought that comes up when I'm at work about owning my organization someday. Last week's conversation with the CEO of the workforce re-entry program also got me thinking about other groups I should introduce myself to, so I'm going to start creating a list for this as I do more research.

In summary, I think this is a good start, and as always, I'm grateful for your support and feedback.

As Colleen processed the first AL entry she had ever written while Meg was in Haiti, she felt a smile melt onto her face as she realized that she had accomplished her Professional goal of becoming the Director of Campbell House. One year after implementing weekly reporting to the board, she was told by Max Carlton that it was the regular reporting and leadership she demonstrated on a regular basis that put her on the board's radar when her predecessor had announced that he was going to retire. She recalled how she kept going over the report to improve it, and continued to reference her progress in her weekly Professional AL updates. Her confidence in sharing this exercise with her team was now extremely high as she saved her doc and looked at the whiteboard. *And now to work on those Career goals and my dream to have my own non-profit and expand the workforce placement programming*, she thought to herself. *I could really use some legal support and make sure I have expertise that can help women gain their independence and stay protected.*

Colleen looked at her watch and realized that she had been sitting in the conference room just reflecting on her AL history for over an hour. She walked back to her desk and picked up her phone to text Meg,

Hey you, what about Stone Capones in forty-five? I have to run a quick errand first, but I think it's a great day to sit on the patio!

Meg responded with a thumbs up as Colleen locked the door to the office.

After leaving the office, Colleen arrived at her next stop. She parked her car in front of the office supply store and walked in quickly. She was focused on picking up note cards, pens, and a new set of dry erase markers for the office before meeting Meg. It wasn't uncommon for Colleen to purchase supplies for the shelter and pay for them out of her own pocket, as there wasn't much left in the budget after meeting payroll and covering other expenses to literally keep the lights on. As she was searching the store for notecards, she heard a woman's voice from the end of the aisle. "Colleen?" the woman seemed to ask. Colleen turned and knew she recognized the woman but did not know her name. "I'm Bryn Miles; we met last night at the Campbell House event."

"Oh! Of course! Colleen replied. "I'm sorry I didn't recognize you; I met so many people last night and should have taken notes or something."

"I completely understand," Bryn replied. "Listen, I'd like to let you know how impressive the event was. My husband and I were talking over breakfast this morning about the positive energy, and amazing amount of support people were giving. I'm still wrapping my head around having met Gloria that afternoon too."

Colleen was smiling and nodding her head, "It was a great event; our team is really pleased. I'll be sure to pass along your feedback."

Bryn placed her basket of supplies on the floor and took a step toward Colleen as she folded her hands. "I was planning on reaching out to you on Monday to talk about an idea I had, but since we're here now ..." Bryn was feeling nervous. "I was so inspired by the stories last night, by Gloria's story ... and well," Bryn paused searching for a way to finish the sentence. "I'm a lawyer."

Colleen stood there, taking this in and wondered what Bryn was trying to tell her. "That's impressive; what kind of law do you practice?"

"Oh, I'm not actively practicing right now. I do small favors for friends and family. I left my firm to start a family, and now that my kids are in school full-time, I've decided to return to the workplace and have been thinking about what I want to do and where I want to do it." Bryn then folded her arms and looked down towards the floor as she continued to search for what to say next. Colleen could tell that she was nervous, maybe even uncomfortable, and was eager to hear what she wanted to say.

Bryn continued, "Here's the deal—I put together a plan to

return to corporate law, but after talking to you, Max, and the other board members yesterday and being moved by Gloria's story, well...that just feels like an empty path for me now. I would like to see if there's a way I can use my experience and help the shelter. I was thinking about the women that come to you with custody or financial issues or are running away from an unsafe home environment but don't know how to protect themselves physically or financially. I'm not sure what the other Goliaths are that you have to battle legally, but I'd love to learn more."

Colleen was stunned; she could not believe what she was hearing. Her eyes grew bigger and started to become misty as she leaned in toward Bryn and said, "Thank you."

"For what?" Bryn replied, "I'm the one coming to you looking for a job—I don't even know if you have a budget for legal services."

Colleen knew Bryn had no idea of her AL Career goals, and how she wanted to start her own non-profit to prioritize the needs of women and leverage her position and opportunity at Campbell House to do so. "Thank you for walking up to me today; thank you for having an open mind and heart about helping us. I struggle with our budget on a regular basis, and right now, we have a few volunteers that provide legal advice and then a few dollars to outsource what's left, but there's a giant gap, and I have a dream of having a set of legal services for women, specifically to address the problems you heard about last night. I can't compete with a corporate lawyer salary, but we can feed your soul."

Colleen gave Bryn her card and shook her hand for what

felt like an hour. She loved how connected she felt to Bryn and didn't want to let the feeling go. "Thank you, I'll call you on Monday," Bryn replied as she picked up her basket and walked down the aisle.

Colleen was still in shock over what had just happened. *I know I am in control of my decisions, but I also believe in fate, she thought. Focus, trust, discipline, and follow-through are all things I need to prioritize in order to meet my goals and manifest what I need, and AL is the tool that guides me. I do believe we create our own luck—God, I can't wait to share this with Meg!* Even though she was eager to get to Meg and share her news, she found herself slowly walking to the register as she was enjoying the replay of her conversation with Bryn.

As she placed her basket on the counter, the man at the register asked, "How is your day going?" Colleen smiled and replied, "Great! You really have no idea."

Stone Capones was in a hundred-year-old building that, at one time, was a hotel with ten rooms and a small bistro. It housed everything from dance studios to art galleries. It eventually found its way back to the hospitality business. It was now a tavern that offered a seasonal menu and provided great service keeping it alive for almost twenty years. Colleen and Meg loved the expanded patio adorned in blooming vines and colorful flora, and were considered regulars as they ate there once or twice a week. "Over here, Cols!" Meg shouted when she saw Colleen walk in. Colleen smiled and headed toward the high top where Meg was sitting.

Colleen couldn't wait to sit down and start sharing. She

placed her purse on the back of her chair and said, "You're never going to believe what happened to me at the office supply store!"

"Hmmm, let's see," Meg replied. "Oh my, God, I know—you bought pencils, no wait...a binder...did you get really crazy and pick up some glue?"

Colleen gave Meg her best "really?" stare and said, "No, smart ass—I ran into someone I met last night at the charity event, and she wants to talk to me about working for the shelter. She's a lawyer that took time off to start a family, and now, she wants to go back to work."

"What!? That's amazing! I hate to be a downer, hon, but can the shelter afford her? You talk so often about your budget challenges, so how can you make that work?"

The owner of Stone Capones broke up the conversation by walking up to the table, "So, how are my two favorite customers?" he asked.

"We're great Clay, and how is business going?" Colleen replied.

"We're stacked with reservations tonight. This awesome weather is really helping us, so I expect a busy evening. What can I get you both while you wait for your server?"

"How about two glasses ... no, wait ... " Colleen looked at Meg and said, "How about a bottle of the pinot gris you served us last time?" Meg's eyes lit up, and she nodded her head in agreement.

"Coming right up!" Clay proclaimed as he headed to the bar.

Colleen started the story of Bryn and how the two women had met at the charity event and connected over knowing Gloria. She then went on to explain what happened at the store while Colleen was shopping. Meg was in disbelief over the connection with Gloria and the coincidence of crossing paths in the store. "Here's to everything happening for a reason, and you being able to drive your dream of helping women in need!" Meg said as she raised her freshly poured glass of wine to toast Colleen.

"Thank you; I'm still processing it all, to be honest," she replied after taking a sip. "Speaking of dreams, shall we start this week's AL review?"

"Can't wait!" Meg replied as the girls took out their smartphones and opened their Google doc. "You're on a roll, Cols; why don't you start," Meg suggested. Colleen took another sip of wine, nodded, and began.

AL for the Week of 8/9:

This week has been dominated by the work required to pull off a world-class gala for the shelter. The additional hours to attend to every detail took a toll on my time, which took me away from some of my Physical and Career goals, but as I write this, the gala is just a few hours away, and I know the team is ready. This helps me feel better mentally, as I know starting on Saturday I can sleep in a bit and rest my brain. My passion and dedication to my Professional life continue to fuel my long-term goals for Career and this notion brings me calm.

Physical – As already mentioned, I did not stick to my regular workout schedule as I was busy working with our extra volunteers and taking time to follow up on the gala details. Meditation was helpful, but I could have done more. I ate poorly as long hours at work found me landing my place in line at the drive-thru. Sleep also took a hit for the same reasons everything else did. It's time to look forward.

- *Looking forward* – Get back to my regular running schedule and waking up each morning to stretch and log my three to four miles. I also plan on bringing my lunch to work and adding protein bars to my snack menu instead of chips. I'm going to look at some new meditation options as I just had a guided meditation app recommended to me. I'm going to experiment with adding a mid-day meditation at the office too.

Colleen waited for Meg's feedback. "I think you're being too hard on yourself given the other demands of your time Cols. You work your butt off staying in shape and eating healthy and are entitled to have a slow week on the Physical front."

Colleen nodded, "I know, and I agree with you. I just feel that if I don't have a strong commitment under Looking Forward, and that I will slack off."

Meg poured Colleen another glass of wine and said, "OK, I hear ya. I'm interested to learn more about this meditation app, but more importantly, let's talk about your sleep. You must shut down the laptop earlier in the evening, babe. I think it would help for you to create a routine, even if it's a simple one, where you commit to getting into your PJs an hour before you want to go to bed and no screens for at least thirty minutes before you turn in. You need to start somewhere."

Colleen nodded her head and said, "I know you wouldn't let me slide on that; I was brief on that topic on purpose," she said, lifting her glass to toast Meg's tenacity. "OK, let's move on to Professional," Colleen said as she picked up her phone.

Professional – Wow! Tons to share here as there was so much enthusiasm and great energy that poured into the prep for the gala. I'm so proud of my team; this is our pinnacle fundraising event for the year, and it's going to be better than ever. The dedication that my team put forth was impressive and so appreciated, especially since we all know how underpaid we are yet stay committed to the soul-filling work we do. I remain focused on growing the team and adding legal support as local policies and regulations around benefits and access to resources are starting to become overwhelming. I can't keep up with the changing laws. I would also love to figure out how to do more with job training and coaching to help our residents build their networks and get engaged with professional organizations that will help them explore new career opportunities.

- *Looking Forward* – I want to reward my team, and I am hoping the investment in sharing the power of our AL exercise will serve as some good personal and professional development training. I need to prepare to introduce this process to my team so I can clearly and simply communicate the power and impact it can have regarding manifesting what you want and achieving your goals.

Meg was beaming with joy and pride as she was so happy for Colleen and knew how great of a job she done to prepare for the gala. "I was really looking forward to talking about the Professional section with you. I'm so proud of you and intrigued about how you're going to share the Accountability Log exercise with your team."

"Getting hungry, ladies?" the server asked, walking up to their table.

Colleen turned to Meg and asked, "You good with the usual?" Meg nodded.

"One margarita flatbread and a split chopped salad it is!" he declared and walked back to the kitchen.

Meg leaned in, "OK, like I was saying, I'm really proud of you, Colleen. I feel like your gala planning woke something new up inside of you. It's hard to explain, but you've had an extra skip in your step for the past month or so, and then embracing the AL idea and wanting to share it with your team really seems to have amplified that."

Colleen was smiling as she looked into the wine glass she was holding with both hands. She knew exactly what Meg was talking about, and she was proud of herself and humbled with the praise. "Thank you. I do feel like there's a new fire in me. It's hard to explain, but the things that I have been focusing on and envisioning are now happening. Look at the conversation I had earlier today with the woman I met last night. That's not a coincidence. At least, that's what I believe and will continue to believe. It feels right, Meg. Things at work feel right. It may be hard to clearly explain what I'm referring to, but I'm reveling in it all and want to keep this feeling at the forefront."

"You're serving as a great example to your team and to me, too, for that matter," Meg replied. Colleen had a giant smile on her face. "OK, now on to Career."

Career – Preparation for the gala gave me opportunities to grow my network as I met leaders from other like-minded organizations that were signing up as sponsors. A few either had programs that focused on women and their professional development or were talking about creating one. I shared my ideas and passion for addressing women and homelessness, and we all agreed to stay in touch. It's interesting how I can almost see a path to achieving my dream of expanding the programs for the residents of Campbell House. As always, it still comes down to resources and getting the funding we need to expand.

- *Looking Forward* – I don't have anything specific this week to focus on from a Career standpoint, with the exception of contact follow-up from new people I met at the gala. Continuing to prioritize my network building and who I know.

"You'll figure out the expanded programming," Meg said as she placed a perfectly cooked square of margarita flatbread on Colleen's plate.

"I know," "And now, with this opportunity to bring experienced legal expertise on board, I'm honestly a bit giddy and overwhelmed at the same time. This woman was also so passionate about working with us. It's something I've been dreaming about for a while; as you know, the legal part of my job is my biggest challenge. It's almost as if everything that went into the gala helped to manifest this opportunity."

Meg put her fork down and reached for Colleen's hand. "Cols, it's your beliefs, your energy, and this exercise that keeps you focused and generates the magic that only you can create. It's one of my favorite things about you."

Colleen raised her glass, "Cheers to the power of focus and AL!"

"Cheers," Meg replied.

The next morning, Colleen was up early as the energy from dinner the night before was still pumping through her veins. She and Meg had an early night because Meg's shift started at five AM, after which she was going to spend time with her mom. As Colleen walked through the quiet house and into the kitchen, she could still smell the coffee beans Meg had ground earlier that morning which brought a smile to her face. She walked toward the coffee pot and saw a folded piece of paper with her name on it next to a picture of a heart. Colleen was smiling even bigger as she unfolded the note.

Good luck today, sweetheart! You are magic, and your team is lucky to have you as their leader. I'm in awe and impressed with you, as always. You Got This!

I love you ~ M

Colleen held the note to her heart and said out loud, "I love you too."

Driving into the office that morning, Colleen's energy started to shift as her usual route was now plagued with construction activity and lane closures. The backups seemed to stretch for miles. As she looked at her watch, she could feel her heart start to race as the team already had a busy day with all of the gala follow-up. She knew they could use the block of time Colleen had asked them to clear on their calendars this morning to tend to the extra work that was waiting for them. Time was really their most valuable asset and one that was difficult to manufacture more of.

As she inched towards the office, she found herself almost at a standstill in a line of cars right in front of the shelter. As she sat there, basically parked, she examined the building and watched the front door as the familiar faces of volunteers came and went, including the faces of some new residents. What struck her this morning were the number of women that were walking in and now lining up at the door. Two had young children by their side, which always broke Colleen's heart. *We need to expand our programming,* she thought to herself. *What can we do to provide more services that will support the parents and their children that come to us?* Colleen reflected on the dreams she had outlined in her Career section of AL each week, but she was anxious now; she was feeling impatient and knew that she couldn't wait to establish her own shelter.

She had to figure out how to move the needle on this concept with the resources she currently had access to, but how? A few of her team members were exploring work placement and training programs; perhaps that would be a good place to start. "Geez, but what about the kids?" she said out loud. "Finding jobs for these women is important, but what about those that need daycare for their kids?" Her increasing angst was then calmed once she realized that traffic was moving again, and she would make it to the office on time after all. Colleen wanted to change her energy before walking through the door, so she took a deep breath and thought of Meg's note. *You Got This!* she thought and felt herself smile as she pulled into the parking lot.

When Colleen walked through the office door, she could see everyone already gathered around the conference room table. She smiled and waved as she quickly walked to her desk to drop off her things, including the supplies she had bought that weekend. As she gathered the dry-erase markers, she thought about her conversation with Bryn and how her desire and focus on increasing their legal capabilities now seemed achievable. A warm feeling ran through her body as she walked into the conference room, more confident than ever. *This is going to work!* she thought to herself as she smiled and greeted everyone with an energetic, "Good morning!"

The team took their seats; she noticed a coffee cup and notebook in one spot, but the seat was empty. "Where's Roger?" she asked. Just then, Roger Wallace walked into the conference room with a giant vase filled with a gorgeous arrangement of yellow, pink, and blue flowers, the colors of the shelter logo. Everyone stood up and applauded as Roger placed the vase in front of Colleen. Colleen's eyes grew huge and began to fill with warm tears as she held her hands over her mouth.

"These are from the board and all of us, Col," Roger shared. "Max wanted to be here, but he had a conflict and could not make it. He asked us to present you with this token of everyone's gratitude and appreciation for your commitment and leadership that resulted in the best gala the shelter has ever had. And I can say, on behalf of this team, we consider ourselves fortunate to have you as our director ... we just love you."

Colleen was shocked; she just kept saying thank you and echoing the mutual respect and appreciation she had for the people sitting in the room. "This was a true team effort, everyone, and the credit for the event's success needs to be shared."

"We are blessed with a list of follow-ups from the event,

but I would like to start today by doing something different and ask that you enter the next two hours with an open mind and a willingness to be somewhat vulnerable." The team nodded and took their seats.

Roger walked over and moved the large vase of flowers to the credenza in the room. Walking back to his seat, he gave Colleen's shoulder a little squeeze and whispered in her ear, "I'm proud of you." Roger Wallace was the oldest employee at Campbell House by both age and tenure. He was a retired police officer that started at Campbell House as a volunteer helping out wherever they needed an extra pair of hands. When he heard that the board wanted to create a full-time position responsible for creating and managing formal partnerships with outside organizations, he jumped at the opportunity as retirement was slower-paced than he had expected. He longed to get back to a regular work schedule. Roger felt that the network of people he had built up over his years as a police officer would serve this role well; he knew almost everyone in the community. He loved his job at Campbell House and was now working with all types of organizations, including churches, corporations, and other non-profits.

Colleen stood up and walked her team through the Accountability Log outline. Her presentation included her and Meg's own personal story and experience with the exercise. She felt her personal story was important to share as she wanted to set the tone and create an atmosphere that allowed her team to feel safe. She knew that in order to get the most out of the exercise, you needed to be open and a bit vulnerable. Vulnerability was important to the success of AL and she wanted to help her team trust the process.

After giving some personal examples, she then wanted to flip the conversation to how the team could apply the exercise to themselves and their roles at Campbell House. "I realize that some of you may be wondering why we are including a Physical component with this exercise, but because of the work we do and the emotional toll that the cases we manage can take on us, it's extremely important that we are strong both physically and mentally." Colleen looked around the table and was pleased to see that everyone was engaged, looking at her and writing notes on the handouts she had given them. She was connecting with them, and her heart was in song. "Any questions?" she asked.

She was confident people had some but she just needed someone to be the first to raise their hand. She decided to turn to her rock. "Roger, you've been here the longest; I would love to hear your feedback on using the Accountability Log to achieve your goals."

Roger nodded, set down his pen, and leaned back in his chair. "I'm an old dog Col, and while I've been around the block more than once and have been exposed to different training via the academy—and yes, this includes training on how to mentally deal with some of the heartbreaking things we would see and hear as police officers. This Accountability Log concept is rather new for me and is something I'm trying to process. Don't mistake my answer for a lack of support for what you're trying to do. I'm a big fan of structure and follow-up. God's honest truth, I feel like I just don't know how to start."

Colleen was smiling and thinking about how to respond when Trudy, their office manager, raised her hand. "Cols, is this something like putting an idea out there that you want to see happen and then managing the steps each week in order to develop that idea and make it come true? I'm thinking goal setting meets manifesting."

Colleen lit up; she loved the short and sweet way Trudy had just described AL. "Trudy, I'm in love with the way you just explained this exercise. Yes, it's about setting a goal and measuring the steps you take each week to meet that goal, but the real power behind this exercise is having a partner that you share these steps with. That's where I believe the momentum behind manifestation starts to build." Colleen paused; the room was quiet. "The reason why I believe this exercise will work for our team is because we already do a great job at collaborating and working closely with each other. There's a lot of trust that comes from the kind of work that we've shared. That, and the fact that there are eight of you, makes partnering easy!" Colleen joked.

"We have a little more than an hour left, so let's pair you with someone and get started on your first entry." Her team took a few moments to look around the conference room table and seemed to easily sort themselves and select a partner. Roger and Trudy were sitting across the table from each other. They each looked up and, with a shoulder shrug and smile, cemented their partnership by shaking hands.

"OK, grab a fresh cup of coffee and then take the next 20-25 minutes to fill in each section on your worksheet: Physical, Professional, and Career. Going forward, we'll use a Google

Doc, but for now, let's just use the worksheet," Colleen coached the room.

"Can I get you a refill?" Roger asked Trudy.

"That would be great, Rodge, I need to figure out how to get started here," she replied as she picked up her pen and leaned on the table, staring at the worksheet.

Twenty minutes later, Colleen entered the conference room and placed her water bottle at the head of the table. "OK, team—five-minute warning, please don't strive for something you think has to be perfect; imperfect is probably better as that means that you've most likely been honest and real about what you've put down." Her team glanced up, then a few of them went back to their worksheets, focused on getting their entries completed. Trudy put her pen down and looked at Roger, who was on his phone.

"All done Rodge?" she asked.

"Yep, sorry Trude – Peg needs me to pick up some things at the store on the way home." Colleen started walking around the table as she coached the room on their next step.

"OK, I now want you to swap Accountability Log worksheets with your partner and take the next ten minutes to review what your partner wrote about. When you're done with your review, let's start with the youngest member of your team and provide them with your feedback. Note that feedback can be in the form of a question about something you need clarity on, or validation of something your partner wrote, or maybe advice if they mentioned something that they need help with. Remember, there are no wrong answers or replies." The room was silent as everyone read their partner's completed worksheet. It then grew louder and slowly filled with the sound of soft chatter as the feedback process began.

Colleen leaned against the credenza and glanced at the beautiful flowers sitting next to her. She bent down to smell a pink rose, and as she stood up, the soft perfume of the beautiful flower lingered in her nose. She looked around the room and saw everyone intently collaborating and smiled at the symbolism of the moment as she had, literally and figuratively, stopped to smell the roses.

Since Trudy was younger than Roger, she was the first to provide feedback. "This was really interesting," she started. "I mean, I've witnessed the power of your network and have always been impressed with how easy it seems for you to find the right people or an organization to fill a gap when we need it, but I wasn't aware that you had been struggling with trying to find job placement partners for so long." Roger nodded his head. "It's also interesting that so many of your Professional goals overlap with your Career goals,"

"Yeah, that was one area where I kinda struggled," Roger replied. "Maybe because I'm already retired, and I am doing something now that's in line with my personal goal of wanting to give back. I feel that the two are really similar to me. It's one thing to find a short-term fix to a problem, like providing someone with a clean and safe place to spend the night or making sure that we have the kitchen stocked with food and equipment to make healthy meals. Those things address short-term needs. We need a way to help our clients help themselves, and that begins with finding them employment. I have talked to so many agencies and corporations, and always come up empty. No one is willing to take a risk on someone that has hit hard times, especially when they don't even have a full-time address."

Trudy could tell that helping the women at the shelter find jobs was something that Roger felt strongly about. "You know," he continued. "One thing this exercise helped me to do was organize my thoughts around this. As I wrote this stuff down, I was thinking about making it easy for you to understand what I was trying to say, and that helped me look at my challenge in a different way. This issue and how to address it have been a constant conversation in my head for over a year. But once I started writing about it, knowing you were going to give me feedback, well...it's like I was able to sort it all out and organize my thoughts into something that could turn into a plan. Writing about it made it more real."

Roger felt vulnerable, but he trusted Trudy and did not feel judged. "I totally understand. It's like you've now put this idea out into the world or universe by sharing it with me. You've given this idea a shape, a body to act on, and now that I know about it, you have to keep defining your steps to meet this goal,"

"Exactly!" Roger enthusiastically replied. They both sat quietly for a moment, taking another sip from their coffee cups as they processed the last three minutes of conversation.

"Colleen is really onto something," Trudy shared.

"She sure is," Roger replied as he held up his mug to toast with Trudy.

Later that afternoon, Roger stopped at the grocery store

on his way home. As he pushed the cart down each aisle, looking for the items on the list his wife had sent, he found himself consumed with the Accountability Log exercise. *I feel like I'm on the edge of something big*, he thought. *What was it about putting my goals down on paper and sharing them with Trudy that made everything seem so real and actionable?* He continued to ponder this as he collected the last few items from the list. Colleen had used the word 'trust' a number of times while she walked the team through the Accountability Log exercise. While Roger respected and had total confidence in his director, his police training often brought him back to that which was black and white. The best cops often talked about having good intuition, and he considered himself part of this group. Whether it was intuition, listening to your gut, or trust, Roger now believed that these were all related and could feel himself getting excited about taking new steps to create a job placement program at Campbell House.

The story he was writing in his mind while he pushed the cart was interrupted by a vibration in his pocket. He grabbed his phone and answered, "Hi, Sweetheart! … Yes, I am in a great mood and have some really interesting things to share with you over dinner … prosciutto and cheese? No problem, I'll grab those now. OK, love you too and will see you soon." Roger felt himself picking up his pace as he pushed the cart; he was anxious to get home and tell Peg about his day.

Roger walked through the garage door and immediately started talking while he placed the groceries on the counter and took off his coat. He couldn't wait until dinner, as he could feel his job placement idea start to take shape. "Colleen hit a home run with an exercise she walked the team through this morning. It was interesting how it forced us to pause and think deeply about what it is we want to accomplish, not just at Campbell House but in our personal lives as well. I really latched onto this idea I have for a job placement program that..."

Roger paused and walked over to the phone he had placed on the counter that was vibrating again. Picking it up, he saw that it was Diana Fredrickson, the liaison he worked with at Grace Community Church and one of the many partnerships he managed for Campbell House. Diana was the one that organized food and clothing drives for Campbell House, and Roger loved working with her. "Oh, no bother, I just walked in the door; you're actually saving me from putting groceries away; it's a perfect time." he chuckled.

Roger walked into the living room and sat on his favorite chair; he couldn't believe what he was hearing from the woman on the other end of the phone line. Could the power of capturing his ideas and goals via the Accountability Log exercise that day already have him manifesting opportunities? "Diana, I don't know what to say," he said as he looked at his wife, who shrugged her shoulders, not really knowing what was going on. "Thank you for reaching out; we're very interested. Oh, I understand you have to talk to your boss and figure out how this would all work. Let me know how the conversation goes and if there is anything I can do to help. Colleen will love it...yep, I'll let her know...no problem. Thank you again...yep...we'll be in touch."

Roger set his cell phone on the coffee table and looked up at his wife, who was now standing in front of him. "Peg, you're not gonna believe this."

4

The Dream Network

Diana

"Caroline! It's time to leave; we're going to be late, honey!" Diana hollered from the kitchen. She was plowing through her typical morning routine of breakfast, dishes, lunch packing, and planning dinner for that night. This was all after waking up over an hour before her daughter so she could shower, take care of the dog, press her clothes, and do an email scan to ensure there were no fires to be put out before she started her commute into the office.

What can I take out of the freezer today that will be easy to make when we get home tonight? Diana thought to herself. She was on the tail end of what had been an extremely long week and wanted to serve her daughter a healthy meal that evening. Long nights after even longer days left Diana both mentally and physically exhausted. As much as she loved the ease of the microwave and meals picked up from a drive-thru, she was feeling guilty about the quality of food she was feeding the person that was the center of universe and wanted to do better that night. She opened the freezer door and thought *Ground beef! Brilliant! We'll make some meatballs, and I'll pick up some pasta on the way home.*

"Caroline Marie! We need to go!"

"I'm right here, Mommy." Diana spun around and realized Caroline was standing in the kitchen doorway. Caroline was Diana's only child. Diana and Caroline's dad had divorced two years earlier, right before Caroline's fifth birthday. It was an unhealthy and abusive marriage, and Diana wanted a better life for her and her daughter. Diana looked at Caroline and cocked her head in wonder when she noticed Caroline had a tortoise in her hands.

"Why are you holding Lester, sweetie?"

"I'm bringing him to school today, Mommy, for show and tell. We're supposed to bring one of our favorite things and tell why they're a favorite thing, and Lester is my favorite thing." Caroline innocently replied.

"Linny, you can't bring live animals to school. It's against the rules, and where will Lester sleep and eat while you're at recess? I think he'd get scared if you had to put him in your dark desk." She was certain she had convinced her daughter to change her mind.

"I'll take him with me; he'll love it outside!" Caroline replied. *Foiled!* Diana thought to herself as she looked at her watch and sighed.

"OK, Linny, it's pretty simple; taking Lester to school will get you into trouble because you'll be breaking the rules. What about the necklace Grandpop bought you with the turtle on it? You can tell the story about the day he gave it to you and then talk about Lester and why he's your favorite thing?" Caroline looked down at Lester with the saddest of faces.

"OK...," she said softly and shuffled her feet as she left the kitchen to put her pet back in his crate. Diana looked at her watch again; *Damn, we're definitely late now*, she thought to herself. As Diana was packing her briefcase, she was again greeted by Caroline.

"Mommy, will you help me put this on?" Caroline asked as she handed a silver chain to Diana.

"Of course, turn around. Now let's get going, OK?" As they both walked toward the garage door, Diana was replaying the conversation with Caroline in her head. *Did I explain too much? Should I have just said no? Did I teach her a good lesson? Why does every interaction with my child make me feel like I could be ruining her emotional development?* Even though Diana had made the right decision by walking away from an abusive relationship, she still had guilt over Caroline growing up as a child of divorce. While Caroline's father, Henry, shared custody of Caroline, Caroline spent the majority of her waking hours with Diana, and it was important to her that she set a good example for her daughter.

"Mommy, what are you going to do today?" Diana looked in the rearview mirror as they drove to school and saw the sweet, young face that had asked the question. She smiled and thought, *she is so beautiful, I'm truly blessed.* "I'm going to go to the office to help people find jobs. I have a meeting with my boss and a new idea I want to talk to him about, and then I'm going to leave and pick you up from school. We're going to go home and make dinner together tonight. We're gonna get our hands all sticky and have fun making meatballs. What do you think about that?"

Diana was expecting the conversation to center around the art of meatball making as she glanced in the rearview mirror again and saw Caroline smiling and nodding her head. "What is your idea, Mommy?" she heard the soft voice ask.

"Well...we'll go home and get all the meatball ingredients out, and then find a big bowl and mash everything together. We can also practice our counting while we roll each ball; it will be messy and super fun!"

"I know how to make meatballs, Mommy; I mean, the idea for your boss."

Diana was shocked; she didn't expect Caroline to pick up on that part of her day. How was she going to simply explain her idea to match candidates with companies that had strong social responsibility agendas? She had been thinking about this concept for years, but the distractions of her unhealthy marriage and then the divorce robbed her of her focus.

Diana was an Executive Recruiter at The Hamlyn Group. She had worked at Hamlyn for five years and was promoted to her current Executive Recruiter role two years ago after starting as an Account Manager. She was hard working and was always at the top of the leaderboard when it came to bringing in new clients and finding strong candidates. Her job was fast-paced, and she loved the high-touch aspect and regular interaction with people, connecting job seekers with opportunities that she hoped would be their dream roles fueled her soul. The money was good, and she took pride in having a long list of happy corporate clients. The satisfaction she received from making a phone call to share the news that a job offer was on the way was priceless.

She was doing well but found herself longing for more. She wanted to use her talent and experience to try something new. She wanted to build something and figure out how to give back to society. After working all day, picking up Caroline, making dinner, and trying to manufacture time to play, Diana was exhausted. She thought that if she could incorporate her passion for philanthropy and social responsibility with her job, she could feed her soul and still have time for Linny.

"Well, you know how we volunteer for things at church like gathering food and jackets for the people at the women's shelter?" She watched Caroline nod her head in the rearview mirror. "That's called charity or philanthropy, and it is extremely important and something that I enjoy. So, I've been thinking about how I can do more things at work that help people, like the ones we help at church. I think it would be great to talk to my clients that have job openings about the people who are looking for jobs. Does that make sense?" Diana turned again to the review mirror and waited for Caroline's response.

"I think so, Mommy. You want to give the people at the shelter a job so they can make money and not have to live there anymore, right? Why would anyone tell you that you can't do that? It's a super nice idea." Diana smiled and basked in Caroline's validation of her concept.

"Thank you, Linny; I appreciate that. There's a little more to it than just giving a job to someone, but you've got the right idea. Let's hope my boss agrees with you!"

"He will, Mommy; you're smart!"

They turned into the school parking lot to join the parade of cars lining up to drop off their kids for the day. Once stopped, the back door of the car opened, and Caroline's teacher's aide greeted them both. "Hi, Mrs. Fredrickson," the young lady said as she waited for Caroline to get out of the car.

"Good morning, and thank you for the white glove service, Melissa. We're not used to having the door opened for us at drop-off."

"I was just walking in and recognized your car, so I wanted to come over and greet Linny, but also thank you for taking the time to come to my house and talk with my mom the other night about her going back to work. You really helped to boost her confidence. I can't thank you enough."

"It was my pleasure; I'm so glad you approached me at Career Day." They smiled and bid adieu as Melissa shut the car door.

Driving away, Diana kept smiling as she replayed the conversation she and Caroline had over the idea she was going to pitch to her boss. "Why would he say no?" she said out loud. "Linny's right!"

Diana walked into her office and was feeling great, with her head held high and her arms full of two flat boxes that smelled of fresh-baked delight. She had decided to make a pit stop that morning after dropping Caroline off to pick up some treats for her team.

"Mmmmm. I could smell Maggie's baked love-in-a-box the instant you got off the elevator," Carl said as he walked past Diana in the hallway. "What's the occasion?"

"No occasion," Diana replied. "I was just thinking how nice it would be to have carrot cake and cream cheese melt in my mouth this morning. The boxes are still warm!" The pair smiled and connected over their love for baked goods.

"Awesome! I'll swing by in ten to claim my fair share," he said as he winked at Diana and continued to walk down the hallway.

Diana loved the team she was on. It was a diverse group of men and women with long tenures at The Hamlyn Group. They were the perfect combination of seasoned professionals and trusted colleagues, and Diana knew she could always count on them to give her honest and direct feedback. Her opinions were always respected, and she always felt like she had a voice. She opened the first box of baked goods, and a soft cloud of sweet smells met her nose. She smiled and thought about the meeting she had scheduled with the team to do a dry run before meeting her boss and VP, Allen Silverton.

"What's the occasion?" she heard a familiar voice ask behind her.

"No occasion. Just felt like a fun way to wrap up the week, and I know everyone is a fan of Maggie's baked inventory."

"Sugar highs and crash naps," Allen replied as he bit into his apple and nodded his head. "It's a sweet gesture, D," he continued. "Ha! No pun intended!"

Diana stood there and watched her boss laugh hysterically at his own comment. *It wasn't that funny*, she thought to herself. *And does he realize just how much of an ass he sounds like at times?* Diana looked at her watch and said, "Yep, pretty 'punny' Allen," then stepped past him to head toward her office. She took a few steps then turned around, "Allen, we're still good for 3:00 today, right?"

Allen took another bite of his apple and, with his mouth full of fruit, he muffled, "Absolutely; I look forward to hearing about this new idea of yours."

OK, that was kinda gross, Diana thought to herself as she shook her head and walked toward her office. It was time to turn her focus on clearing her mind before she met with her team.

Walking into the corner conference room, Diana was greeted with smiles and praise as everyone in the room had heard the rumor of Maggie's bakery coming to the meeting. "Good morning, everyone!" Diana said with a smile on her face and enthusiasm in her voice. "Who's hungry?" she asked as she placed the boxes in the middle of the table and began to set up her laptop. "I'd like to take a different approach to today's meeting, as I've prepared a pitch for Allen to introduce a new business model which would directly impact your roles. Now, don't get nervous; the treats are not a way to soften the blow of any bad news but more of a celebration of the confidence I have in all of you and how we can join forces to help people in need by coaching them on how to secure employment."

Diana took a pause as she scanned the room and watched her team wash down muffins and bear claws with coffee and tea. She was proud of the nine people in the room that now reported to her and also proud of the fact that she was their leader. The abuse of her previous home life while married to Henry had crushed her self-esteem and optimism for a long time. She knew she was destined for more and was proud of the fact she could leave her unhealthy marriage and now financially support herself and Linny.

Her team began to nod their heads and she could tell they were leaning in, curious to hear what she had to say. Excited about the non-traditional approach she was about to take with her presentation, Diana tapped her laptop and displayed a black screen on the wall. With a click of her mouse, the room started reading the quote in a white font that appeared on the slide.

> It is literally true that you can succeed best and quickest by helping others to succeed.
>
> – Napoleon Hill

"We all know that we spend more time at work than we do at home," Diana began. "This is hard to dispute and leaves me hoping that the majority of you like your jobs and find happiness in what you do. As members of the same team and being honored to lead you, my goal is to prioritize your success and to ensure your job satisfaction here at Hamlyn. That said, I'd like to ask that you have an open mind as I walk you through the next few slides."

Diana clicked the mouse again, and the image of a red and beige building constructed with brick and stone was displayed on the screen. The building was large and had wooden stairs that led up to a wood porch that extended the length of the building. Some of the windows were curtained, and some had half-drawn blinds. While not run down, it was apparent that the building had aged. "This is Campbell House," Diana started. "Some of you are aware of the fact that I lead a volunteer group at my church that supports this women's shelter. Campbell House provides transitional housing and training for women who are working through a personal crisis such as losing their home or trying to escape domestic violence. Campbell House provides limited time-period stays which vary from a few months to two years."

Diana paused to get a read of the room. Her team looked engaged, which confirmed that they were connecting with what Diana was telling them. "You know, I've driven past that house dozens of times and never knew what it was. My daughter takes ballet at a place about a mile north of this building. Are you asking us to volunteer there?" Maria, one of Diana's account managers, asked.

"No, well...not exactly. My ask is tied to our responsibilities here at Hamlyn. Let me work through the next few slides and further explain." Diana quickly realized that she would have to get clearer on what her agenda was before meeting with Allen. She didn't want to confuse him with this slide. "Please, keep the questions coming as this is helping me tighten up my story for when I present this again to Allen this afternoon."

As she advanced through the next few slides, she displayed pictures of some of the shelter's residents. She told success stories of each person, including their background and the programs they had at Campbell House to overcome their hardships. "One of the programs at Campbell House is job placement. Anywhere between one and three months before a resident moves out of the home, they receive training, interviewing, and job search assistance. It's one of the most important programs that the shelter has, as employment is the sole way for these women to become financially independent. Most start with entry-level, hourly jobs as they build up their experience, and to be quite honest, their confidence. There are some that come in with previous job experience and are ready to take the fast track towards a career re-launch, and unfortunately, the resources at Campbell House don't exist to help this group."

Diana took another pause and scanned the room again. Additional head nods gave her the validation she was looking for. Maria smiled and said, "So this is where we come in; now I think I see it."

Diana grinned and said, "Thank you for the great segue; here's what I'm thinking," Diana went on to explain her vision of having a Hamlyn Group-sponsored program whereby her team would design and support what she was calling, The Career Table. The Career Table would be a place where screened residents would work with Diana's team to inventory their skillsets, experience, and long-term goals and match them with additional training programs that would accelerate their skill development. Corporate scholarships would help fund the training, after which the resident would be connected to an internship or what she called a "returnship" program within that corporation.

"How would we get started?" Carl asked.

"Once Allen approves the program, I would like to reach out to our list of corporate clients and schedule a meeting to present a version of these slides and appeal to their desire to build a socially responsible program that scales. We know how much companies pay us to find top talent; well, this would be a value-add that we would be providing them. Kind of a 'Social Responsibility as a Service' offering. The cost to them would be the scholarships that each resident would use to accelerate their skills development and complete more training, but it ends up being an investment in securing an employee that will start out loyal and grateful for the chance to get back to work. We screen, coach, and find strong candidates for our customers to consider and help simplify and jumpstart the process."

Maria raised her hand, "What's in it for Hamlyn?"

"Two things. First, this would be a value-add differentiator that we would offer at no additional cost. All the client has to do is invest in their training which they already do with everyone they hire. This allows us to interact with each corporation at a different level, and deepen our relationships with them, and build trust. The benefit of stronger relationships and greater trust and loyalty is an increase in business. Heck! This could lead to us unseating some of our competitors that we share clients with. Second, I believe this is a great way to approach new clients with fresh messaging. None of our competitors are doing this. Let's face it; every recruiting firm has the same value prop at the end of the day; The Career Table is how we can differentiate ourselves. Doing good while doing well and keeping the process simple and easy for our clients is magic."

Diana could feel herself light up as the excitement and love for this program was growing in her soul, which was definitely shining through as she talked with her team.

"How does this tactically and logistically work? I mean, I love the idea of offering a program that can improve our customer relationships and differentiate us from our competitors, but what are your expectations regarding the impact on our current workloads?"

"Great question, Sanjay; thanks for asking. This is an extremely important point as I'm not looking to increase the number of hours that you currently put in. I've included a couple of ideas to address the management of additional work and cycles this program may cause. To start, I think it's important for Hamlyn to participate in their own version of The Career Table and sponsor our own set of interns. While not account managers, these people can definitely help you scale by taking care of your daily tasks and groundwork. It's important that we speak to our firsthand experience and success of running this program as well." Diana was proud of the fact that she was totally prepared and able to answer everyone's questions.

The next click of her mouse brought the presentation to an end. Maria started the applause, and the entire team celebrated Diana's idea. This show of support gave Diana the boost of confidence she needed before walking into Allen's office. "I'm so grateful for you all, and I want to thank you for having open minds regarding this program. If you have any concerns at any time, please let me know."

"Keep bringing us Maggie's, and we'll agree to just about

anything!" Carl added.

Diana felt great after her team and was ready for a late lunch. Back in her office, she opened a plastic container that contained chicken salad she had brought from home. As she sat at her desk and enjoyed her meal, and she read through her notes a few more times. She had added more structure to the beginning of the presentation to clearly set the stage for what she was asking for. The time with her team was truly invaluable.

OK, it's 2:45 and time to roll, she thought to herself as she cleared her desk and unplugged her laptop.

Walking down to Allen's office, she could still feel the excitement, pride, and joy that had carried over from her meeting with her team. She was confident most of them would be open to this idea but wasn't sure if the entire team would be on board. The feel-good vibe she was experiencing had her smiling as she turned the corner toward Allen's office. As she approached his door, she could see that it was closed.

Diana caught Allen's attention as she stood on the other side of the glass wall that bordered his office. Allen threw up a finger to motion that he needed a few more minutes. While she was a little early, after twenty minutes had passed, she could feel her high energy turn to frustration. *He's just robbed me of fifteen minutes*, she thought. The negative attitude was definitely impacting her, and she wanted to make sure she was at the top of her game. She caught herself and thought of her conversation with Linny that morning. Replaying her sweet voice in her mind as Linny had belted, "Mommy, you're smart!" Diana grinned as she stared out the window, waiting.

The opening door snapped her attention, "Did I miss something funny? Allen asked.

"Uh, nope—was just thinking about my daughter," she replied as she walked past Allen to enter his office. She walked over to the small meeting table in the corner of the room and set up her laptop. "Do you mind if I connect to your monitor?" she asked as she pointed to the large screen on the wall.

"Ah, a formal presentation!" Allen exclaimed, "Why not another PowerPoint today?" *Keep your cool, Diana...* she thought to herself.

"This isn't a garden variety presentation, Allen; I'm confident you'll find it quite refreshing." With a few taps on her keyboard, the Napoleon Hill slide was on Allen's monitor.

It is literally true that you can succeed best and quickest by helping others to succeed.

– Napoleon Hill

"Hey, Napoleon Hill! I'm a big fan. Have you ever read his book, Outwitting the Devil?"

"No, I have not, but his work is definitely timeless," Diana responded. She quickly thought to herself *Is there some crazy irony in this conversation?* She had decided to take out the slide that included her presentation agenda and instead walked over to Allen's whiteboard. "Here's what I want to cover with you today," she said as she reached for the blue Expo pen and wrote:

Increasing our value to our existing clients

+ Differentiating ourselves from the competition

= Top Line Growth.

"Elevating our value proposition and the relationship with our clients is what I'm going to talk about today," Diana proudly shared.

"You have my attention," Allen responded.

Diana thought to herself, *YES! Great start, girl; now keep going.* She then wrote on the board:

To increase our client value and differentiate ourselves from the competition, we need to ...

"Finish the sentence," Diana requested.

"What?" Allen replied.

"Help me finish this sentence – before I dive into my idea, I'd love to confirm what's most important to you and ensure I'm aligned with your priorities." She was a master of this sales approach and knew how important it was to get as much up-front buy-in from your audience as possible.

"Well, now I feel like I'm at a board meeting, but I like it and will play along. I would say provide the best customer service and increase our understanding of each client's needs so we can prescriptively service them. Be creative in solving our clients' biggest problems while maintaining operational efficiency and increase our top line. How's that?" Allen replied.

"Awesome," Diana said as she captured his input on the whiteboard. She knew exactly how to tie her agenda to what Allen thought was important now. Popping the cap back on the marker, she walked over to her laptop to continue driving the conversation with her slides.

When she finished her review of Campbell House and the concept of The Career Table, she took a pause as Allen had been pretty quiet, sitting in his chair with his arms now folded. "Any questions or impressions?" she asked.

Allen paused then said, "So, how many people live at Campbell House, and what do you think the average number of candidates each quarter would be eligible for these internships?"

"Great question. There are seventy-five residents at the home right now, with almost eighty percent working with the current job placement program. That gives us sixty residents. Based on my knowledge and experience working with Campbell House, approximately seventy percent of those residents would be well positioned to benefit from The Career Table program, which means forty-two candidates." Diana had done her homework and expected Allen would ask this question.

"That's great to start with, but what about scaling the candidate pool; what would the future number of candidates look like?" Allen asked. Diana reminded Allen that The Career Table program would be piloted at Campbell House because of her relationship with the organization.

"I have contacts at the director level Allen, and they're good people I know would support Hamlyn's pilot of this program. Once we work the kinks out with a subset of our customers and the residents at Campbell, we can rinse and repeat at other transition homes. That's how we scale."

Allen sat quietly. Diana was eager and nervous to know what he was thinking. "Is there anything else?" he asked.

Diana realized they were close to time, and she had to leave to pick up Linny in thirty minutes. She quickly ran through the questions and feedback from her team meeting earlier that day and then went in for the close.

"I appreciate your attention, time, and questions today, and I realize we are at time. Before we wrap up, can you think of any reason why we can't move forward with this pilot program?" Diana asked.

"I need to think about it, Diana. This is new concept, and I applaud your passion and creativity, but I'm not sure it's the right time for Hamlyn to launch something like this. I'm not saying you don't have my support, but I think we need to sit on this right now and pick the conversation back up in six months or so when we're planning next year's budget. I want to minimize distractions for the team right now as they are doing so well."

Diana's heart sank; she had shared numbers that showed how the program could self-sustain in just three months and was struggling to digest what she was hearing. She was out of time and didn't know what to say. She wanted to lash out and speak her mind, but she knew that was a poor idea. "Well, I'm disappointed to hear this, Allen, as I met with my team, and they had high levels of confidence in the success of this program. At least you didn't 'shit-can' the entire concept, and as you said, we'll see where we're at in six months from now." She thought to herself, *Did I just say 'shit-can'? I really need to leave, like right now.*

"Very well, Diana, thank you for your time," Allen replied.

Diana packed up her laptop and exited Allen's office with her spirit broken and her gut full of disappointment. She was hoping to get to her office and make an exit without seeing anyone, but as she walked closer to her door, she saw Maria glance her way and stand up from her cube. She smiled and walked towards Diana's office, entering just before Diana stepped in. *Don't ask, don't ask...*Diana thought to herself.

"How did it go!?" Maria asked, full of enthusiasm. Diana sat down and flashed Maria a broken smile.

"Well, at least he didn't shit-can the idea." Maria gave Diana a confused glance, and Diana went on to explain how the conversation at the end of the meeting went and how Allen suggested they table the idea for six months until the next fiscal budget discussions begin.

"I'm sorry, Diana," Maria said with a solemn tone. "I understand that a 6-month push with the dependency on how next year's budget conversations go means nothing for at least 9 to 12 months, if at all."

"Yep!" Diana blurted as she stood so she could start packing her backpack and leave on time to grab Linny.

"Don't give up on this, Di! The longer I'm in this business, hell...any business, the more I realize that organizations are not doing enough to give back and support the communities and industries that they serve. This is such an important program, one that can actually change lives. I gotta tell you; I have not stopped thinking about it since your presentation earlier today." Diana zipped up her backpack and walked over to her door to grab her coat off the hook.

Sliding her backpack over her right shoulder, she turned to Maria and said, "I can't tell you how much I appreciate you saying that, Maria. It was the boost and well...validation I needed to flip my mindset before picking up Linny."

Maria smiled and said, "I know you have to bolt; just know that I'm around to brainstorm and talk about this anytime you need me."

"You're the best! I appreciate you, but I do need to go." Diana waved, and they both smiled as she walked toward the elevators.

There's a reason for this hurdle, Diana thought to herself. *At least I took the first step to put this idea out there.* She was now deeper in thought and could feel herself growing hopeful. There was still a sense of doubt as she opened the door to her car and tossed in her backpack. *I just don't know what to do next*, she kept thinking as she pulled out of the parking garage.

The pickup line at school was shorter than most days, which gave Diana a sense of relief as she was afraid she was going to be late. The door opened, and she heard the sweet sound of Linny's voice. "Hi, Mommy!" she belted as she settled into her seat and clipped her seatbelt tight.

"Hi, Champ!" Diana replied, "How is the most special and most smart young lady I know today?" Diana looked in the review mirror and melted at the sight of Linny's smile, which was short one front tooth.

"Thanks, Mommy, I'm good, school was fun, and we started a new project today. I need some art stuff to finish it up. Ms. Sweeny gave us a list that's in my bookbag."

"OK, great! I love doing projects with you. Let's dive in after we go home and start our meatball effort." Diana replied. She glanced in the rearview mirror again and saw Linny, still smiling and nodding her head in agreement.

As they pulled into the garage, Diana made a promise to herself to be present with Linny while they made dinner. She wasn't going to allow the disappointment she had experienced earlier that afternoon slip into their time together. "Go wash your hands and meet me back in the kitchen." She heard the plop of Linny's backpack on the kitchen table and the sound of small feet running up the stairs of her townhome.

Diana walked over to her desk in the corner of their family room and started to take her laptop out to plug it in, and stopped. *No, I said I wasn't going to do anything but be present,* she thought to herself and dropped her bag on her chair. She walked into the kitchen to find Linny pulling her lunchbox and folders out of her backpack as she started the afterschool routine Diana had established, which included wiping out her lunchbox and placing papers or assignments for Diana to review on the kitchen table.

"Mommy, look at this!" Linny exclaimed. Diana walked towards the table after flipping on the light.

"That's pretty cool, what is it?"

"The class is making dream posters, and this is a picture of the one Ms. Sweeny showed us, so we know what ours are supposed to look like."

Diana picked up the paper that had a picture of a poster board with photos, words, and inspirational sayings on it. "Wow, I love this idea. What are you supposed to put on your board?"

Before Linny could answer, she started reading the short explanation at the bottom of the page.

Dream Big Project

This is your chance to think about what your biggest dreams are. There is no wrong answer, as your thoughts around what you want to be when you grow up, where you want to live, and even the people who you want to be around are your own special thoughts. Cut out pictures from magazines or print things from the computer or even draw something. Everyone will have the chance to tell their story and present their board to the class.

This is pretty cool, Diana thought to herself. "Linny, this sounds like an awesome project. I can't wait to help you with it. I'm going to get the meatball stuff out so we can talk more and get our hands messy. What cha think?" Linny nodded and started to clear the table. Diana pulled the step stool up to the counter to get ready for her young chef to start the meal preparation. Linny walked back into the room, ready to start.

"Do you want to crack the egg?" Diana asked. Linny smiled and grabbed the first egg to start the process. Mashing breadcrumbs, ground meat, and seasonings, Diana began to ask Linny about the pictures she wanted on her Dream Board.

"Well, I want to start with a picture of a fireman and then a teacher and then an ice skater because those are all things I want to be when I grow up."

Diana paused, "A fireman? I didn't know that's where did you get that idea from?"

"I want to help people, and I saw a story on the news about the lady fire chief, and I thought that was cool." Diana nodded in acceptance and was secretly celebrating her daughter's choices.

"What else?" she asked.

"Well, I know she's not a real person, but I would like to have a picture of Belle on my board because it would be nice to have a best friend like her someday. She's smart and likes to read like me and gets picked on but she is still happy. I also would like Mulan as a friend because she's so brave and strong." Diana loved what she was hearing. "Taylor Swift and someone who wants to be a doctor would be good too. Maybe I'd like to be a doctor when I grow up. Ms. Sweeny said there are no wrong answers, so I'm just going dream big and find good pictures."

Linny held up her meat-covered fingers like they were claws to Diana, "Want me to tickle you, Mommy?" They both laughed and started to clean up after putting the meatballs in the oven.

"I have a stack of magazines you can look through for pictures, and we can also print stuff from the computer if you're missing anything." Diana grabbed a pot to start boiling water for the pasta and thought, *Maybe I should do a dream board too.*

Later that evening, after kissing Linny good night, Diana walked downstairs to tend to some work on her laptop. She glanced in the kitchen and saw remnants of magazine clippings on the table. Walking in to tidy the table up, she paused and picked up one of the pictures Linny had found of a doctor and then one of Taylor Swift and wondered, *What would my dream list of friends look like...what would my dream network look like?* She didn't know exactly what she was feeling, but it was positive and had her curious and eager to invest in this idea. She sat down at the table and grabbed one of the blank sheets of paper Linny had been drawing on, and wrote at the top:

My Dream Network

Her thoughts were all around the business model she had pitched that day, the concept of The Career Table that she had fallen in love with and did not want to wait the six months to see if it would get a chance to turn into something real. *Who are the people that could best mentor me, people that could relate to what I'm trying to build and have advice about how to start?* She tapped the colored pencil on the kitchen table and pondered this for a few moments. "Man, it would be great to talk with someone who is also a single parent, a professional, and is looking to change their career or do something new," she said out loud. Her energy was shifting; she was thinking positively and feeling hopeful. She was having fun and wanted to dig deeper.

She sat at the table for almost an hour before she finally put the pencil down and stood up to review the list of names and titles that she had captured in purple.

- Single parent - Working full-time and looking to make a career pivot.

- Business owner – Has gone through starting a business a few times.

- Chief Human Resources Officer – Firsthand feedback from my profile customer.

- Real Estate Agent – Get smart about sub-leasing costs and explore options for training centers.

- Melinda Gates – Powerhouse in the non-profit space and humanitarian.

- Adam Grant – Love his writing and outlook.

- Brene Brown – Just because!

Hmm..., Diana thought to herself as she stepped away from the table and turned to walk toward to countertop, where an open bottle of wine seemed to smile at her. Diana popped open the cork and watched the cabernet fill the glass. She felt confident and happy about what she had just done, and as she stood there smiling in the kitchen, she thought *There's something here, I'm not sure what exactly, but I can't ignore this feeling of hope and intrigue I'm experiencing.* She grabbed her list, written in purple colored pencil, and her glass of wine before walking over to the couch to continue to contemplate what her next steps were going to be.

"Mommy..." Diana opened her eyes to the sweet sound of Linny's voice that was now serving as an alarm. Diana sat up and realized that she had fallen asleep and had spent the night on the couch. "Why aren't you in bed, Mommy?" Linny asked.

Diana glanced past Linny at the coffee table, where she saw her list and half of the wine still left from the evening before. "You know, Linny, I sat down on the couch last night after you went to bed and dozed off. I guess Mommy was more tired than she thought."

"You're, silly Mommy, you're not even in your PJs!" Linny giggled.

"You think that's funny, do ya?...I'll show ya funny," Diana grabbed Caroline and pulled her on the couch for a tickle party. It was Saturday morning, and the duo had a busy day. "Let's get you some breakfast before I get into the shower," Diana said as they both walked into the kitchen.

Caroline opened the pantry and grabbed the box of Cheerios while Diana grabbed the milk and Linny's favorite bowl. It was a bowl that she had painted during one of their pottery store outings. Linny had placed small happy faces all over the bowl, which made Diana grin every time she picked it up. Diana realized it was symbolic of how she felt when she had fallen asleep and had also woken up. She embraced this feeling of joy and said a quick prayer of gratitude while she walked up the stairs to take her shower.

45 minutes later, Diana was standing at the garage door, "Let's go girlfriend!"

"I'm waiting for you, Mommy!" Diana heard faintly through the garage door. She opened the door to see Linny sitting in the backseat of the SUV. "Well, my apologies for making you wait Lin; do you have everything?" Caroline nodded her head to confirm that she packed her swimming gear as they were headed to class at the YMCA.

Pulling into the parking lot, Diana said, "Remember, Daddy's picking you up today from swim lessons and will bring you back to our house tomorrow night after dinner."

"I remember, Mommy," Caroline replied.

Once inside, Diana walked her daughter to the side of the pool where her class was starting, kissed Linny goodbye, and then eagerly left to get to her next stop.

As Diana pulled into the parking lot of Campbell House, she again found herself smiling. She had another load of clothes that included extra jackets to drop off that had been collected at her church. She was eager to talk to Roger as the disappointment she felt on her drive home from work the day before had turned to hope, and she was anxious to share her experience and ideas with him.

"Hey, Di!" She heard as she was walking into the center. Roger's energy was always high, and everything he said always sounded joyful.

"Hi, Rodge, I've missed you," she replied as she walked over and gave him a hug. "Once we get done unloading my car, can I buy you a coffee? I have something I'd like to talk to you about."

"Sure, you don't have to twist this old guy's arm," Roger enthusiastically replied.

Once at the coffee shop across the street, the pair settled into the couches that were staged in a far corner of the store. Before Roger took his first sip of black coffee, Diana started in. She told him how the presentation with Allen had gone. She could see a small bit of disappointment in his expression, as their conversation the night before had left him hopeful that they would be able to pilot Diana's idea at Campbell House. He had confidence in the concept and was certain that the residents of Campbell House could benefit from what she wanted to roll out. Diana knew this and wanted to deliver the unfortunate news first. Roger shook his head in understanding and was more disappointed for Diana than he was for his own program, but Diana wasn't upset. She was actually smiling, and Roger could tell there was something more. Diana's energy was high, and Roger felt himself leaning in.

"I'm sorry to hear how things went with your boss Di." he shared.

"It's good, all good. And to be honest, I can now admit that I wasn't surprised. It's OK, as something else happened once I got home with Linny that has me excited." Diana told Roger about Linny's project and the epiphany she had after their dinner.

Roger was now looking at the piece of paper that held Diana's Dream Network list. He looked up and smiled at Diana. "This is very interesting, Di, I mean—it's a very simple yet powerful way to create a vision board of sorts. You know, the residents at Campbell are often working on building their self-esteem and determining what their next step should be with regards to getting employment; my only fear is that they may feel overwhelmed."

"What do you mean?" Diana asked.

"Well, hear me out. Again, I love the idea, and even at my old age I would like to draft my own Dream Network, but the women we work with at the shelter have been through tough times and feel hopeless, not worthy, and often betrayed and abandoned. These types of life experiences take a toll. You have Brene Brown on your personal list, and I actually know who that is as my wife is a huge fan. I understand why you would put her name down, but I can't imagine someone who is so unsure of themselves being comfortable thinking big like this. Listen, I'm in and want to work with you to include a version of this in our Back to Work programming. I also love the name 'Career Table' and am committed to working with you. I just want you to realize that not everyone is you, Diana. Your energy and confidence are both high, and I know what you've overcome to get to where you're at. This was probably easier for you than it will be for some of our residents because of your existing network. Let's work together to figure out how to address this challenge and build lots of Dream Network lists."

Diana sat and processed everything Roger had just said. If she was honest with herself, she was a wee bit deflated but completely understood and respected where he was coming from. He wasn't discounting her idea; he actually was embracing it and was asking her to consider some different points of view.

She took a deep breath, "You're right; I totally understand how important this different point of view is. I'm happy to invest more time into this concept and work with you to create something that's applicable and relatable for the women at Campbell House." She was feeling strong and confident.

"Hey! Before we wrap this up, I can help you with some of the folks on your list right now." Diana gave Roger a puzzled look. "The business owner and Head of HR that you wrote down...I have an idea."

Diana now realized what he was talking about, "Of course, sure— – what are you thinking?" she replied.

"First, you need to schedule some time with Max Carlton. He's on our board, and he's a powerhouse. He's in real estate, so it might also check the box to know someone in that industry, but he's also a very good guy, a humanitarian, and big supporter of Campbell House."

"Yeah, I know of him but have never met him," she replied.

"I'll send you his contact information. Reach out to him and grab a coffee—you can thank me later. And then there's my Claudia,"

Diana nodded her head as Roger always spoke so highly of his two daughters. She knew one was in healthcare and the other in an executive role in business, but she didn't know where. "Sure, I'd love to hear about your daughters," Diana replied.

"Claudia is head of Human Resources for one of the largest insurance agencies in the US. She also serves on our board and is just brilliant. I'm not just saying that because she's my daughter, you know...well, that might have something to do with it."

"Wow, Rodge, an introduction would be awesome!" she enthusiastically replied. "I have so many questions to ask about the value of a program like this at a large company, including how I scale candidates and address the specific hiring needs of each organization." Diana felt her energy rising again. *Geez, I've shared my list with one person so far, and this is what happens?* she thought to herself.

"She's local, and I'm certain she would be open to chatting with you. Peg and I see her almost every Sunday night, so I'll tee something up for you and then send you her email to follow up. How's that sound?"

"Like a gift from heaven, Roger, thank you so much, and thank you for the great feedback on the Dream Network concept. I'm going to process everything and create a version that will land well with the women at the shelter. Let's grab another coffee soon," Diana replied.

"You got it – and don't forget about Max as a contact. Would you like me to make an intro? As the president of our board, he's very familiar with the work your church does, and I'm confident he'd be happy to have you buy him a coffee."

"Peg's one lucky lady, Roger! Your thoughtfulness is world-class and is something that I value about you," she replied. Roger flashed her a huge and humble smile as they got up from their chairs.

"I'm here to help you, Diana, and I really believe in this concept," he said, opening the door as they left the coffee shop.

Walking back to her car, Diana felt like she was on cloud nine! *What a difference a day can make*, she thought to herself. *I went from massive disappointment to incredible levels of excitement and hope!* She knew Roger's validation (and to be honest, his thoughtful challenges) were feeding her in amazing ways. Her confidence was high, and her commitment strong for defining the next version of her business model and the Dream Network.

As she pulled out of the Campbell House parking lot she kept thinking about how she was going to spend the rest of her day. She needed to rework the Career Table concept to incorporate the Dream Network idea, making sure to remember the feedback Roger had given her. She wanted to make sure this pilot resonated with the women at Campbell House.

Driving home, she found herself lost in all kinds of visionary thinking and then paused. *What does this mean for my work a Hamlyn?* She instantly felt heavy, stressed, and uncomfortable. *This sucks....* she thought to herself. *Do not let thoughts of Allen or that meeting interfere with the positive feelings you've built today.*

As she considered how the thoughts of working with the women at Campbell House made her feel versus her job and future at Hamlyn, she began to wonder, *Am I in the right role? I still have a lot of time on this planet, and do I want to spend it working in a job that brings me frustration and angst or one that brings me joy?* It was hard to admit, but she knew she had to move on from Hamlyn. She also knew that if she was honest with herself, she could have predicted how the presentation to Allen would go. The conversation with Roger was enlightening and was exactly what she needed. *How can I use my skills and make a difference in this world? How can I be a great role model for my daughter? How can I do this and ensure I'm fiscally responsible?* As these questions swirled in Diana's mind, she again felt a smile form on her face. She knew what to do, and part of it was throwing caution to the wind, but as scary as it felt —what felt better was that she knew it was right.

Pulling into her garage. she thought about what she was going to do with her evening. *I'm going to work on the Dream Network outline for Campbell*, which seemed easy and obvious as she walked through her door. *Time to call Linny and wish her good night."*

Sunday morning was met with high energy and a short list of household jobs that Diana wanted to complete before Linny was dropped off. She enjoyed her morning coffee, sitting in the warmth of the sunshine coming in through the living room window that smiled on her while she relaxed on the couch and planned her schedule. Clean the house, start laundry, and get to the grocery store before her daughter got home – all were at the top of her list. The only thing bugging her was the desire to manufacture more time to work on the Dream Network outline and what the Career Table program could look like for the residents of Campbell House.

Diana was definitely distracted, and wondered how important it was to get the floors washed that day. She was also haunted by thoughts of Hamlyn, Allen's expectations, and the follow-ups that she had to do just seemed silly to her now. *I just have to prioritize*, she thought to herself. *Shut the F up and prioritize, and the Hamlyn crap doesn't make the cut.* She got off the couch to start her morning by checking the box on as many household chores as possible.

It was almost 11:30 when she finally paused from vacuuming and realized she was hungry. *I definitely need to eat before I go grocery shopping*, she thought and turned off the vacuum. She then felt her jean pocket vibrate from her phone ringing. She pulled out her phone and didn't recognize the area code. She assumed it was spam, but something told her to answer. "Hello, this is Diana."

"Hi Diana, this is Claudia Nichols— I'm Roger's daughter and got your contact information from him today—how are you?"

Caught off guard and a bit in shock, yet pleasantly surprised, Diana replied, "Great to meet you, Claudia! I think the world of your dad, and am so grateful to meet you!"

Now what?! Diana thought to herself. *How awesome that Roger followed through with his commitment, but I feel totally unprepared for this conversation.*

Claudia graciously grabbed the virtual mic, "Diana, I realize it's the weekend, and I'm sorry to call you on a Sunday, but my folks and I have a standing Sunday brunch, after which I typically dive into an early start on my work week, but I didn't want to neglect following up with you after talking to my dad."

"Claudia, this is totally fine. I'm happy to not only talk with you but also to meet Roger's daughter. I can't say enough great things about your dad."

"He does kick ass, doesn't he?" Claudia responded. "He could just sit in a rocking chair and celebrate all that he's done but refuses. What I admire about him the most is the fact that he has a huge heart and continues to aspire to give back." If Diana didn't admire and love Roger a ton already, the conversation with his daughter was confirmation that he was an amazing guy.

"I appreciate the call, Claudia, and would love to know more about what you and your dad talked about. What did he share?" Claudia went on to talk about a program she was struggling to launch that focused on corporate social responsibility and what their organization could do to make investments in the communities that they served, including programs that would support the career development of individuals that would not have simple nor easy access to job training.

"I love the sound of what you were talking about with my dad, and I would love to learn more. Are you available to meet for lunch in two weeks? I'd love to talk about developing my own Dream Network, too - what a brilliant concept!." Diana was numb and stood still, stone-faced in her hallway with one hand still on the vacuum cleaner.

"Um, yes—Claudia I would love to meet you and talk through this model more. As your dad can attest, I feel strongly about the power of networking and have a ton of faith in how it can help people. It's a very scalable idea that can change the way organizations manage their hiring practices ... gawd, am I sounding too corporate?" Diana feared.

"All good, Diana, I'm pretty casual, but I would like to ask you one last question."

"OK," she replied.

"I know you are full-time employed by Hamlyn Group, but are you able to contract for your services outside of Hamlyn?"

"Not at this time. I have been seriously thinking about how to go out on my own, as I pitched this idea to my management and was shot down. I know it's good and can help a company differentiate themselves; I just haven't decided what to do with it."

Diana couldn't see it, but Claudia was smiling and nodding her head. "Let's talk next week when I'm not infringing on your valuable personal time. I don't have an open headcount right now, but I would love to talk about a contractual position. It would come with no guarantee for a full-time role but could push you closer towards your personal goals."

Diana's skin was tingling as she wanted to start jumping on the couch in celebration. "Sounds great, Claudia; I'm open on Thursday and Friday and look forward to coming to the conversation with an open mind."

"Awesome!" Claudia replied." My business manager will be in touch." Ending the call, Diana finally let go of her grip on the vacuum and sat down on the floor. *Holy crap, it's happening...I can do this* she thought to herself as she sat there, filled with fear and anxiety. She got up, leaving the vacuum plugged in, and walked toward her desk in the family room. She sat down, opened her laptop, and thought, *How do you start a letter of resignation?*

5

Lead From The Bench

Claudia

"Hmmmmm..." Claudia found herself saying out loud as she stood in the middle of her large, walk-in closet and tried to determine what to pack for her trip to Miami. *Sticky and humid outside and refrigerator cold inside always makes packing for these conferences a challenge, she said* to herself as she pulled items that would be easy to layer and then shed as needed. A few moments later, she heard the heartwarming sounds of her twin girls shouting downstairs, "DADDY!" followed by the sound of small feet running towards the front door.

Patrick had just come home, and Claudia could feel her soul smile. Patrick was her best friend and biggest fan. She knew she was unconditionally supported by him and appreciated how much he had contributed to building her confidence and overall career success. She lifted the hanger holding a pink and cream herringbone blazer and left the closet to walk towards the bed to lay it next to a pair of cream pants. "Do I need anything underneath? Maybe just my gold and pearl necklace to complete the look!" Claudia skipped to her jewelry case to finalize her outfit for the panel she was moderating in a few days when giggles and sweet sounds of laughter rose from the stairs.

"Hi, beautiful."

Claudia heard as she turned around with a huge smile on her face to find Pat with two eight-year-old girls at his side, fighting for his attention. Claudia walked toward her husband and greeted him with a big hug and kiss. "Hi-ya, handsome! Welcome home, just packing for Miami." Claudia and Pat were each other's second marriage, and while each had a child from their previous marriages (each of their sons were in college now), they longed to share the experience and love of parenthood together, and were blessed with twin daughters after a short stint with invitro. Their families were wonderfully blended as the boys loved having little sisters to dote over, and their daughters, Grace, and Erin loved having big brothers. Claudia knew she was blessed with an amazing family, and she gave thanks for it every day.

"Yeah—I knew you'd be occupied with getting ready for your trip, so what do you think about ordering pizza and having a picnic in the family room?" Claudia melted, Pat was always thinking ahead, and this idea was yet another example of this thoughtfulness. Claudia would often feel guilty about managing the demands of being the Chief Human Resources Officer for a Fortune 500 company and being there for her girls. She wanted to serve as an example and role model for how women can have it all, yet accepted the fact that this wasn't a reality. She was committed to doing her damndest to find balance and manage the compromises that came along with being a working mother.

"I'm tall like mommy," Claudia heard as she turned toward the closet to find Erin trying to walk in her blue suede pumps. She smiled and walked over to Erin and placed the pearl necklace she had just pulled from her jewelry case around her daughter's neck.

"There...now you're ready for business," Claudia said, leaning down to kiss the top of Erin's head. It was important to her that her daughters felt supported and empowered to dream big and go after every goal they set for themselves.

"OK, ladies, who wants to help me order the pizza for tonight's picnic?" Patrick asked. The joyful response from his daughters jumping up and down and raising their hands, sent a wave of love through his body as he put his hand over his heart and looked over to Claudia and smiled. The trio walked out of the bedroom and headed downstairs. "Hurry up, Mommy!" She heard Patrick shout, "The pizza usually takes an hour or so, and we can't promise that we can save you any...just sayin'."

"Oh, I'll be down sooner than that!" Claudia declared. "Don't count on eating my share." She walked towards the doorway of the bedroom. "Hey, Pat?" She could see him turn around at the bottom of the staircase.

"Yeah, babe?"

"How about a happy hour in thirty?" she asked.

"Sure....what color? I'll have it ready," he enthusiastically replied.

"I'm feeling brown tonight." She got a thumbs up from her husband and walked back to the closet to complete her packing. Claudia loved public speaking and serving on panels. Turning this activity into a career was a personal goal of hers and was something she had been thinking about for years. As the CHRO of The Hemisphere Group, she had become very popular with conference and panel planners as her experience and stories around hiring, leadership, mentorship, and career development were rich and always captivated the audiences she presented to.

She walked over to her jewelry chest for one last accessory to compliment a slim black dress with a matching blazer. Opening the top of the cabinet, her hand passed over a row of stud earrings and stopped at a red and gold pin. Claudia picked up the cardinal and held it gently in her hands to allow the light to bounce off the small set of rubies that were set in the cardinal's wing. Wearing this pin always made her feel grounded, as she was reminded of her upbringing and the challenges her mother went through as a single parent to her and her brother. She came from modest means, and this pin was her mom's most prized possession. Her mom couldn't afford to pay for Claudia's college tuition, so she worked hard to put herself through school, always trying to save extra money to give to her mom. She was proud of where she came from and how her mom served as an example of great perseverance and strength. Even though it had been seven years since her mom had passed away, she still missed her dearly. She again thought how important it was that she served her daughters the exact same way her mom had served her. *This is perfect*, she said to herself, grabbing the pin and walking back to her suitcase.

She could hear the ice clink in the glasses as she walked down the stairs. Claudia sat down at the island and watched Patrick fill two rock glasses with bourbon from the crystal decanter they were gifted on their wedding day. "What's the current flavor?" she asked.

"Bardstown this time," he replied. She smiled as he knew this was one of her favorites.

She picked up her glass as he took a seat next to her and said, "A toast to my amazing husband and father of my children—I honestly wouldn't be where I am without you."

Patrick leaned in and gave her a kiss. "I love you too," he replied before taking his first sip. "So, what is this event you're headed to?"

"It's a conference for women in the insurance and financial industries. The programming ranges from industry expert-type roundtables to career development workshops and mentorship programming. I'm moderating a panel of male leaders from the industry called; Women, Financial Services and Leadership—The Male Perspective."

"Sounds misogynistic, babe," Patrick replied.

"Yeah…a few folks have shared your same opinion, but to be honest, I love the format and the fact that the agenda is provocative. We need more men to serve as allies in our male-dominated industry, and the guys on the panel have great stories about women they've either worked for, managed or both. My interviews with them uncovered some amazing lessons that I'm eager for both men and women to hear."

"I love your passion," Patrick replied after standing up to respond to the sound of the doorbell so he could collect the pizza that was waiting for his family. Claudia also got up and headed into the family room, where she grabbed a blanket off the back of the couch to spread out on the floor.

The next morning, Claudia woke up to the sound of her phone buzzing on the nightstand. She reached over and slid the button on her alarm app to Dismiss. It was 4:00 am, and the house was dark, quiet, and asleep. She slowly sat up and pulled the sheets over Patrick that had slipped off during the night. Stepping out of bed, her thinking went into list mode as she engineered her schedule based on the arrival time of the car that was taking her to the airport. *Pickup at 5:30, showered and dressed by 5:00, send my status report and update my calendar by 4:45, out of the shower by 4:20. OK – but first caffeine!*

With her coffee mug in hand and still in her pj's, she left the kitchen to head toward the den to do a quick email check and print up her notes for the panel. She placed the mug of black coffee on the cover of a notebook, contributing to the design of coffee rings and watermarks that made an art deco type of pattern. The mug was a Mother's Day present from the girls and was wrapped in photos of them making funny faces at the camera. It was her favorite. *OK, let's print these interview notes and then check email*, she thought to herself. As the hum and clicks from the inkjet printer played in the background, Claudia leaned into her laptop screen as she read the email from Max Carlton about the transition of the President of the board at Campbell House.

I'm writing to let the board know that David Marton will be stepping down as Campbell House's Board President. David's leadership will be dearly missed as he elevated the programming of Campbell House and accomplished things that no one could predict. David's departure has been prompted by a move to Ireland within the next six months to fulfill a lifelong dream that he and his wife Renee have had for the past twenty years. We celebrate this next chapter in David's life and wish him and Renee nothing but the best. David's formal transition will begin in two weeks and will be the primary agenda item for our next board meeting.

Regards,

Max Carlton

Woah! Claudia thought to herself. As Vice President of the Campbell House's board, she, Max, and David had often talked about the time when he would step down, and Claudia would take over. She had been a board member for more than five years and was responsible for developing strategic committees that were now expanding Campbell House's offerings and community reach. *This wasn't supposed to happen for another twelve months!* Claudia thought to herself. *Damn, time to figure out what this position is now going to mean to my overall workload.*

Claudia glanced at the time on her computer screen. "Shit!" she said out loud. She had been so consumed with processing Max's email that she lost track of time and was now fifteen minutes behind schedule. She quickly pushed back from her desk and jogged upstairs to jump in the shower.

Ready to leave, she gingerly walked down the stairs with her suitcase, trying not to wake anyone up in the house. She set her Samsonite by the front door and turned to find Patrick holding two warm cups of coffee. "OMG, did I wake you? I'm sorry,"

Claudia said. Patrick handed her the mug from the girls filled with fresh coffee and said, "I always want to kiss you goodbye before you leave Claud's. When I came downstairs, I saw the light in the office and realized that you hadn't packed up your laptop— are you running behind? Shouldn't the car be here in ten?"

"Yep! You're right. Thank you for the coffee; I didn't have a chance to finish my first cup. I was caught off guard by an email I received from Max."

"What's up?" Patrick asked.

"Can you follow me while I drink this down and pack up my laptop, babe? It's big news." As Patrick followed her into the office, Claudia shared the details of Max's email and what was going through her head.

"Well, are congratulations in order?" he responded.

"Not officially, not yet. I need to talk to Max and figure out where his head is at with regards to the transition plan and how we'll pull the rest of the board into this." Claudia was rushing around the office and making sure she had her notes, phone, laptop charger, and anything else that would be necessary to make her trip a success. She was excited about being the board president and was already thinking about new initiatives she wanted to introduce to the board to define how they could expand their program offerings. A flash from the headlights of the car pulling into their driveway lit up darkness outside of the office door. "I gotta go," Claudia said.

"I love you; let me know once you've landed at the hotel," Patrick replied. Claudia walked toward the front door, grabbed the handle of her suitcase, and turned to blow him a kiss.

"I love you more!" she whispered as she walked out the door.

In the car, she sent an email to Max to reply to David's announcement.

Hi Max! Wow— that was an interesting announcement to wake up to. I'm so happy for David and Renee and their ability to accelerate their retirement dreams. I'm headed to Miami today to moderate a panel for the Financial Professionals Association (an all-male panel focused on women in leadership in the industry—you would love it), so I'm tied up for the next two days, but I would love to grab a drink when I return to discuss David's transition plan. Let me know if you can make time Thursday or Friday of this week to connect.

Already looking forward to it!

Claudia

She hit Send and then rested her phone in her lap. *What an exciting way to start the week!* she thought to herself. She couldn't stop thinking about taking on this new role. "Now to focus on my panel prep," she said out loud and put on her headphones for a quick meditation.

Once at the hotel, Claudia could feel herself getting into the zone as she stood in front of the mirror in her hotel room and practiced her panel introductions. She had interviewed the panelists ahead of time and was excited to have them share their stories with the audience. She was passionate about the concerns surrounding the low numbers of women in senior positions in the banking and insurance industries and was committed to creating awareness around the lack of programs to address this.

"Thank you again for your time today, my name is Claudia Nichols, and I'm the Chief Human Resources Officer at The Hemisphere Group. It's my honor to moderate today's panel - Women, Financial Services and Leadership: The Male Perspective." She went on to share the stats she had gathered on the decreasing number of women in leadership roles in the industry as she wanted to stress why this topic was so important. "It's now my pleasure to introduce you to our panelists."

She set her notes down on the desk and gave herself a nod in the mirror. *You got this!* she said to herself and then began to pack up her things to head to the conference center downstairs.

Walking into the meeting room, Claudia saw a number of familiar faces. "Clauds!" she heard from the far side of the room.

"OMG! Kathleen! I didn't know you were going to be here!" Claudia exclaimed. The two walked toward each other and shared a long embrace.

"I've been looking forward to this since I had the twins. I

mean, I love my babies and all, but it feels great to be at an event where I don't have to worry about navigating a stroller and carrying a diaper bag," her friend replied. Claudia and Kathleen met years earlier at a similar conference and had stayed in touch as Claudia served as mentor and coach to Kathleen when she needed extra career support. Last year, their bond increased once Claudia found out Kathleen was having twins.

"Are you back at work full-time?" Claudia asked.

"I didn't have a choice, Clauds. In order to stay on the management track, I had to come back full-time, as my part-time options would have been a step back in title and pay. It hasn't been easy as I feel like management is holding the fact that I'm a mother of twins and have bigger demands on my personal time over my head."

"That sucks. Listen, I want to hear more, but I have to get my mic on as I'm moderating a panel in this room in thirty minutes. Drink at the end of the day?"

"That's why I'm here! I saw your name on the agenda and knew I had to come to this event. The panel title sounds awesome; I'm looking forward to it," Kathleen responded.

Claudia gave her another hug. "I love you. Thank you, let's catch up later tonight," she replied and headed towards the stage.

The panel was a huge success as Claudia could feel the energy of the audience as they asked both thoughtful and challenging questions. She knew this was a positive sign that the panelists' stories had landed well. Inundated with praise and positive feedback as she walked toward the exit of the meeting room, Claudia was beaming inside and felt her confidence and ego grow. She felt accomplished, important, and deserving of her career success and title. She also appreciated that she had a supportive husband that celebrated her career growth. She wondered about Kathleen and how she was managing her work/life balance. *Maybe I should ask her if she wants to re-start our mentoring conversations*, she thought.

On her way back to her room, she checked her phone and saw a text from Max.

> *Got your email; Thursday works— I also have*
> *an update to discuss.*

Update? What does that mean? Claudia started thinking too much. *Is it the timeline? Could it be about backfilling my role? Maybe David still wants to stay involved somehow?* She was overthinking each question and could feel the worry building as she grabbed her key to swipe the electronic lock on her hotel room door.

The flight home was short and simple, and for the first time in a while, Claudia chose not to open her laptop and instead listen to Bach while she made quick notes about becoming the President of the Board of Campbell House on a notecard. She wanted to be prepared and organized when she met with Max on Thursday and knew she'd have little time between her job and catching up on the two days lost with the girls.

✓ *Launch new educational programming
and find a committee chair.*

✓ *Distribute the employee and volunteer survey.*

✓ *Meet with Campbell House leadership, including the Director.*

✓ *Move board meetings to monthly for the next quarter
to build momentum.*

✓ *Plan a board team-building activity and ensure everyone
is still connected to our mission and vision.*

Her mind was racing, and her excitement around the role was building as she continued to build her list. *Geez, not sure how much time Max will have on Thursday*, she thought to herself. *I can easily turn each of these bullets into a 20-minute discussion.* She put her pen down and closed her eyes to listen to Prelude in C Major.

"Clauds! Over here," Claudia heard when she walked into the restaurant. Max was sitting at the end of the bar with a martini glass in front of him.

Claudia walked up and gave him a hug before setting her purse on the bar. "Angels Envy—big rock, please," she asked the bartender before adjusting her stool and settling in for her conversation with Max.

"How was the panel? How was Miami?" he asked.

"Absolutely awesome. I knew from my prep interviews that the event would be hit, as each panelist had fantastic stories of women they had either worked for or managed; the audience loved it."

"What was your favorite story?" Max asked.

Claudia took a sip of her bourbon and said, "Well...the unconscious bias guy, I think! There was one guy that is a VP of IT now and leads a team of over eighty people. He told a story about his previous role with the same company where he was a director and on a team of five that had four men and one woman. He talked about the culture of the company and how much it promoted diversity and inclusion, including how his manager at the time was one of the strongest proponents of the agenda in the company. Well, it was bring-your-kid-to-work day and everyone was convened in the cafeteria, waiting for lunch to be served. He was standing with his team when a couple of unsupervised kiddos were getting rambunctious in the corner. This manager guy turned to the one woman in the group—not any of the men—and asked her to go over and mind the kids and quiet them down. My panelist shared that he later pulled his manager aside to call out what had happened because he knew this woman was annoyed. This guy responded in horror and admitted that he didn't consciously ask her, but that it just seemed obvious to him at the time that she should be the one to take care of these kids."

"Wow, it really makes you think about how often this happens; I mean, how often do I take action based on unconscious bias?" Max replied.

"I know, right?" she responded and held up her glass. "A toast to managing our unconscious bias and a toast to David and the new chapter of his life." The two clinked glasses and each took a sip. "Not trying to change subjects here, but on the plane ride home, I started jotting down some core ideas about the president role and how to get started." Claudia started.

Max carefully set his glass on the bar and leaned in. "Yes, I've been waiting to talk with you about this, and I'm glad that we're having the conversation in person."

Claudia suddenly felt a heaviness come over her; it was worry. "Is everything alright, Max? Does this have to do with the text you sent me regarding an update?" Max was nodding his head in confirmation.

"It does. David's early resignation has accelerated conversations regarding the committee model we started talking about last year."

Claudia was now the one slowly nodding her head. "You mean the re-org discussion about trimming the executive roles and having more committee chairs?"

"Yep, that's the one," Max replied. "The other board members reminded me of this last week, and after a conversation with the director of Campbell House, I think it's a good idea."

Claudia was feeling lighter. "I agree it makes sense; it also means that you don't have to worry about selecting my backfill," she replied as she took another sip of her bourbon.

"About that Clauds, there's been a few other inquiries about David's replacement." Claudia felt her head turn and tilt forward as she processed what Max had just said. "The conversation about going to a committee chair model has brought talks about succession planning and selecting new leadership. There is another member of the board that would like to be considered for President."

It wasn't heaviness that Claudia felt next, but annoyance sprinkled with a bit of anger. "Who?" she asked.

"Christine Montgomery."

"Christine?! She has been on the board for less than a year." Claudia barked.

"I know, but she's been a good contributor and comes with a full resume of non-profit board experience. Listen, Claudia; we do our best with a shoestring budget we have, and need to appreciate every resource we have access to. Everyone respects your tenure with the board and admires your leadership. It's not like people are aggressively voting against you being President. I realize this is a shock, as we've discussed you potentially taking the role in the past, but with Christine raising her hand and showing interest, I think it's important to be fair and open about this. I'm sorry that this is such a surprise."

Claudia looked down at her glass and took another sip. Setting the glass back on the bar, she started to circle the rim with her finger. "OK, you're right. This is a surprise. But at the end of the day, I truly want what's best for the board and serving the residents of Campbell House." She wondered if she was starting to sound like a politician. "So, what does this mean exactly? How do you choose between Christine and myself?"

Max finished his martini and motioned to the bartender for one more. "Would you like another?" he asked. Drinking her last ounce, she nodded yes as Max began. "I'd like to have you both give a presentation to the board regarding your vision for Campbell House, including programming around new ideas to serve more residents. I'd also love to hear your thoughts on fundraising and partnering with other organizations to tap into their programs and volunteers. Your thought leadership is great, Claudia - I know this is something you can nail."

Claudia was still absorbing everything Max had just shared. She picked up her second glass of bourbon and raised it for a toast. "To leadership, teamwork, and striving for what's best for the board and Campbell House!" They both took a sip, and she asked, "When do you want us to give our presentations?"

Max put his hand on her shoulder, "Thank you, your contributions to the board have been amazing. I really appreciate your understanding and look forward to your presentation, which we'd like to see next Thursday." Claudia smiled as she and Max started a new conversation about the difference between bourbon and whiskey. "That's why I drink vodka, so I don't have to remember details like this about what I drink!"

The conversation was definitely lighter, but in the back of Claudia's mind, the combination of confusion, wonder, anxiety, and a little bit of worry was starting to build. *Five years on the board and a huge commitment to the mission. An executive at my company leading an amazing team. A professional speaker full of creative ideas. And still there are questions about me being President? Ha! I've got this!* She thought to herself as she finished her second drink.

That weekend, Claudia worked on her presentation every evening after the girls went to bed. She wanted it to be full of life and inspiration and motivate people to think outside the box. She wanted to demonstrate leadership and emphasize the importance of strong levels of collaboration. She hoped to make every person on the board feel important and that their opinions mattered. It was Sunday night, and as she sat at her desk Googling inspirational images and quotes to compliment her slides, she felt a hand on her shoulder and a kiss on the top of her head. "Hi, babe, how's it going? Can I get you anything?" Patrick asked.

Claudia turned in her chair, "I'm close, and it's going well. I would love to share a glass of wine when I'm done. Can you give me fifteen? I would also love to do a dry run of the presentation with you, if you don't mind."

"You got it!" Patrick replied as he walked out of the room. Fifteen minutes later, Patrick returned with a bottle of wine and two glasses that he set on the edge of Claudia's desk. "Ready?"

"Perfect timing; I'm more than ready for a glass and to review this with you."

"Sounds great," he replied as he sat on the loveseat across from the desk with a full glass of cabernet.

Claudia clicked through each slide and practiced her messaging. She had delivered thousands of presentations over the years, but this one felt different. She was nervous and couldn't figure out why. With her dry run completed, she grabbed her glass and sat next to Patrick. "You know, I can't explain it, but I'm kinda anxious about this. I have this strange nervous energy that I haven't experienced in a long time," she declared.

"Could it still be some of the shock from your conversation with Max?" Patrick asked.

"I'm not sure. Can't nail it. I don't know this Christine very well and while she's had some good ideas over the past year, I don't know her leadership style and just can't see her as President. I know that sounds awful." Claudia shook her head, disappointed in herself for even thinking that "Here's the deal, at the end of the day, I'm confident that I will win the vote. Maybe I'm just nervous about things being awkward between us once this is done. Does this make sense?" she asked, and Patrick nodded yes.

That week, Claudia went through her routine, getting the girls ready for school, team meetings at work, lunch appointments, and then home for family dinners. The week was going smoothly, yet she found herself distracted each day by the thought of the presentation. *I've got this; I bring more experience and leadership to the table than Christine ... what am I so nervous about?*

Thursday arrived, and Claudia was rehearsing her presentation on the drive to Campbell House. She felt strong and confident as she pulled into the parking lot and chose a space right next to Max's car. Before heading to the general-purpose room where the board usually met, she decided to take a walk around the facility, soak up the energy of the shelter, and think about the programs she wanted to launch. Her thoughts focused on the employees, volunteers, and residents. She knew the organization was doing well, but she strived to do more. Standing in the lobby, she heard her name called from behind her. "Excuse me...Claudia, nice to see you." a tall woman with blond hair said, walking through the lobby. "I know we don't know each other that well, but I'm excited about today and looking forward to our presentations."

"Hi Christine, yes!" Claudia replied. She was caught off guard but appreciated Christine approaching her. The two shook hands and made small talk about the new paint color in the lobby.

Christine looked down at her watch, "It's almost time, shall we?" she asked as she motioned towards the meeting space with her hand. As the two women entered the room, Claudia could feel her nervous energy start to build.

"Hello and welcome!" Max exclaimed as the women walked in and took seats on opposite sides of the large table. "While we wait for the last few board members to arrive, why don't one of you get set up? Who would like to go first?"

Claudia lifted her hand, "I'm happy to go," she replied.

"OK, I've got the projector plugged in and ready for you—why don't you set up at this end," he responded as he removed a chair that had been placed at the head of the table. Claudia had already taken out her laptop and stood up to relocate and connect to the projector. Her slides were ready, and she felt confident in her pitch, including the details about how the board could support new programs while staying within their current budget.

The last two board members entered the room and took their seats. Max looked around the table and gave the room a nod, "OK, let's get started. I'd like to thank all of you for making the time to attend this special board meeting as we celebrate the next chapter of David and Renee's life and welcome his replacement as President of the board. I would also like to recognize the contributions and investments both Christine and Claudia have made to the board and the Campbell House mission. You've both been outstanding board members, and regardless of who ends up filling David's spot, I look forward to your continued involvement and support of our goals." Max went on to explain the basic format for the meeting, which included both women giving their presentations, which would then end with a vote. "OK, Claudia. Thank you for going first. The floor is yours."

Claudia stood up and, with a click of a remote, launched her presentation. The kickoff slide had an amazing old picture of Campbell House, which she used to set the stage for the journey she was about to take the room on. Her story and goals were perfectly delivered as her voice was full of passion and high energy. Assuming Christine's presentation would be a standard set of slides that included facts and stats, Claudia focused on making her presentation feel more like a photo album than a corporate communication. Each slide included an inspirational quote and image that she hoped would differentiate her presentation and connect with the hearts of the board.

"In closing, please know that it has been my honor to serve on this board and support the mission of Campbell House for the last five years, including serving as your Vice President for the last two. Thank you for your support and time." The head nods and smiles were abundant as the team around the table softly applauded Claudia's presentation.

Max took over, "Thank you, Claudia, that was amazing. You obviously put a lot of thought and time into this, and I'd like to share just how much I appreciate your passion."

"Thank you, Max; it was a fun and soul-filling exercise to do. Christine, the floor is all yours." Claudia replied as she unplugged her laptop and pushed the video cable toward where Christine was seated.

"Thank you, Claudia." Christine then reached over and turned the projector off. She stood up and slid the chair that Max had removed from the head of the table back to its original spot. She sat down and placed her arms on the table with her hands folded and smiled at the room. *What the hell is she doing?* Claudia thought to herself.

"Are you going to present to us today, Christine?" Max asked.

"Yes. I'm totally prepared to talk with you all about my interest and passion for being your President," Christine replied. "I've just chosen not to use slides and make the communication of my vision, ideas and drive around my plan as personal as possible, and I'd like to do that by simply talking with you today."

Is she out of her freaking mind? Claudia thought. *Does she really care about this role and presenting herself as a strong leader? We're supposed to be giving a presentation, not having a fireside chat.*

Claudia was now back at her seat, settled in for what she expected to be a train wreck. Christine began and was sincere and articulate. She talked about the board elevating Campbell House and its brand on a national level. She continued to describe the ways they could increase programming, funding, and volunteers. Claudia found herself leaning in with the other board members and wondered, *What did it take for her to prep for this, and is she going to remember anything she's telling us right now?*

"Thank you for your time and consideration," Christine concluded. "If you give me the honor of leading this board as your president, you have my word that I will prioritize the Campbell House mission and give this role one hundred percent." The room was engaged and clapped as Christine stood up from her chair and walked back to her original seat.

Max again took the floor, "Thank you, ladies, for two outstanding presentations. Your visions reflect everything this board and Campbell House needs to continue to change the lives of our residents. I know I speak on behalf of everyone in this room when I say thank you for everything you have done. Alright, now it's time to vote. You each have a piece of paper in front of you. I'm going to ask you to write the name of your preferred candidate, then fold it in half. There are no losers here; I want to reinforce that. We are all leaders and are now looking to identify the person who will chart our course. Once you're done, I'll collect your ballots."

Claudia's heart was racing. There were nine people voting, so there was no chance of a tie. *Christine's speech was good but was it something that demonstrated real leadership and clear vision?* she wondered.

Max collected the ballots and walked over to a small table in the corner of the room. His back was to the room, and Claudia could hear him unfold each piece of paper. Claudia felt awkward and was fidgeting in her chair while she waited. He turned around and again thanked the ladies for their speeches. "We have a winner by one vote. Congratulations to Christine Montgomery, you are the new President of the Campbell House board!" The room clapped, and Christine smiled and held her hands together in a namaste position.

"Thank you so much, and thank you, Claudia, for making me a better board member and now leader; I appreciate you and everything you have done for Campbell House. You're a true inspiration." Claudia forced a smile while joining the applause.

"Congratulations, Christine, that was an inspirational speech you gave." She was dying inside and physically felt warm as feelings of disappointment, sadness, embarrassment, and anger started to brew. *What the fuck just happened?* She asked herself. *How do I exit this place with grace when all I want to do is scream right now?* Her questions and inability to process the fact that she had just lost left her feeling numb and paralyzed. *Shit, fuck...pull yourself together*, she coached herself as she packed up her laptop. *You need to hold your head high. At least until you get to your car.* She looked over at Max, who gave her a reassuring smile, but it didn't work. She wanted out of the room, and she wanted out quickly. It was already late in the evening, so she was grateful that people were anxious to get home.

She walked over to Christine and waited her turn to shake her hand and congratulate her before leaving. "Congratulations, Christine, your speech was great and obviously was well received." Claudia did her best to paste a smile on her face.

"Claudia, I mean...thank you. That means the world to me, and I want you to know that I loved your ideas and look forward to supporting you and executing them with the committee model we'll be launching soon."

"Congratulations again," was all Claudia could come up with as she turned and walked out of the room.

It was raining out, which Claudia was grateful for because she now had a reason to run to her car. She opened the door, threw her backpack on the floor, and raced to put the key in the ignition. She could hear her phone blowing up with text messages, most she assumed were from fellow board members and most definitely one from Max. She was upset and just wanted to get out of the parking lot and find her way home. Pulling into her driveway, she stopped before opening the garage door. She wasn't ready to talk about what had happened yet. She now felt heartbreak and turned the car off and sobbed.

Five minutes later, the garage door opened, and she saw Patrick walking toward her down the driveway. She rolled down the window and wiped her nose on her sleeve "Jesus, Clauds, what's wrong?" he asked.

"I didn't win. The board chose Christine," she replied. "I honestly can't explain how I feel right now and how shocked and upset I am." Patrick put his hand on Claudia's tear-soaked cheek,

"Come inside, babe; I'm here to listen." Claudia nodded and pulled the car into the garage. Once inside, she walked upstairs to wash her face and change into her pajamas. Drying her face with the hand towel, she looked at her puffy, red eyes in the mirror and couldn't escape the feeling that she had failed. It made her want to cry again, so she coached herself to think about something else as she walked downstairs to meet Patrick. He was sitting at the island, quiet as he wanted to give her space because she was obviously upset. As she reached for the box of tea from a corner cabinet, she started the story of how the meeting went. It was a play-by-play, including her initial thoughts when Christine had turned off the projector and pulled up a chair.

"I couldn't fucking believe it," she said. "I thought, what are you doing? How is this approach going to be effective? But the joke's on me as the board obviously liked it more. "Don't get me wrong, she was sincere and smart and told a great story. Damn, the more I think about it, the more I realize just how good and brilliant she was. Perhaps the better man did win. I don't know; I just wish I could shake how freaking shitty I feel."

Patrick stood up and gave her a hug. "You're one of the strongest women I have ever met. I know it sounds lame, but I trust there's something to learn from this, and in time, you'll figure out what that is." He was nervous as he wanted to tell her everything was going to be alright, but he knew in the near term, that wouldn't be the case.

The next morning Claudia woke up feeling exhausted and drained. After getting the girls off to school, she chose to keep her pj's on and plopped herself down at her desk. She re-read the sea of texts that filled her phone the night before.

> *Your presentation was great and your ideas were excellent, Claudia! Great job!*

> *Please know that it was a very hard decision, Claudia – both of you were so excellent. I look forward to continuing our journey together. The board needs your leadership."*

Text #3 was from Max...

> *I know you and know you are disappointed. I can only reinforce how valuable you are to the success of the board and how much your energy and leadership are needed to meet our goals.*

Blah, blah...whatever, she thought to herself. As she took another sip of lukewarm coffee, she felt more disappointed. *What the hell, girl?* she thought. *Get over this and move on. You're an executive, for Christ's sake, and need to get your head back in the game.* But she couldn't figure out what to do next or how to shake the feeling of being disconnected from the board.

Just then, her phone buzzed. *Who is this?* She thought as she didn't recognize the number. A tap on her phone opened up the message from Christine.

> *Hi, Claudia, it's Christine. I'm reaching out as I would really love to talk to you, preferably sometime today. Can you find twenty minutes?*

Claudia stared at her phone. *Why does she need to talk to me?*

Claudia quickly replied..

> *Hi Christine, I'm free from 11-12 today. Let me know if that works.*

Minutes later, her phone buzzed again...

> *Great! I'll call you then. Thank You!*

Blah, blah...whatever Claudia thought to herself before deciding to distract herself with email.

Later that morning, Claudia was in the kitchen when she heard her phone ring in the office. She looked at the clock. "Shit—I forgot about Christine," she said out loud as she was elbow deep in making cookies and still in her PJs. She raced to the office and caught the call just in time. "Hello, this is Claudia," she answered.

"Hi Claudia, it's Christine. Thanks again for taking my call and replying to my last-minute request."

"No problem, I was just finishing up a meeting and had this break in my morning." she replied and thought *Ha, with chocolate chips, eggs, and flour.*

"Listen, I appreciate this conversation may feel a bit awkward, but I wanted to check in with you and get your thoughts regarding your role going forward. I would really like to figure something out around you leading all of the committee chairs and building the workplace program you discussed. I'm in love with your ideas, and to be honest, as I listened to your presentation, I felt that you and I are more aligned than you and David were. Due respect to David, that is." Claudia listened and liked what Christine was saying but still felt a sting.

"What are you asking exactly?"

"I'm not one hundred percent sure, Claudia, but I'd love confirmation that you're open to taking on another board leadership role, given the VP role will be retired with the new model."

That's right... Claudia thought to herself. *Where is my place on the board now?* She instantly felt resentment, rejection, and a touch of anger from feeling unappreciated. "You know Christine, I really appreciate this conversation and your feedback, but last night's decision made me pause and think that perhaps everything worked out the way it was supposed to."

"What do you mean?" Christine asked.

"Well, I have a very demanding job, and with twin eight-year-old girls, my plate is full. I remain committed to Campbell House and its mission, but I have been thinking that it may be time to step down from a leadership role and serve the board as someone at large."

"Sure...I respect that." Claudia could hear the disappointment in Christine's voice. "Family comes first, and there's no question that your high-profile job means additional demands. What if we don't come to a decision right now but give it some time and talk again in a week. I'm not ready to give up on this yet." Christine chuckled before pausing to hear Claudia's response.

"OK, that's fair. Let's block this time next week and continue the conversation. I appreciate you reaching out." Claudia ended the call and, in the back of her mind, felt she had already made her decision. She had no desire to consider Christine's ask. But she didn't know why.

After ending the call and looking at her phone, she noticed how it was coated in flour. She looked around the kitchen, then down at her pink pajamas and said out loud, "What the fuck are you doing?" She turned and went upstairs to change her clothes and her attitude. Pulling her running shorts from the dresser she could feel her mood lift. *A good run is exactly what I need to shake this.*

After double tying her running shoes, she skipped downstairs to grab her headphones. Standing on her front porch, she grabbed her phone and went to one of her favorite podcasts, *Dare to Lead with Brene Brown*. As she scrolled through the list of episodes, searching for something new, the words "New Rules of Leadership" caught her eye. *This seems massively relevant*, she thought to herself and hit play. The podcast was an interview with the US Women's Soccer team all-star Abby Wambach. Abby had released a book called *Wolfpack*, which was a compilation of leadership lessons learned throughout her career as a professional athlete.

As Claudia channeled her inner Olympian, she started her run at a freakishly fast pace. Listening to the amazing insight from Abby that poured from her experiences on the field and how she struggled to get the same recognition and pay as her male soccer counterparts was really interesting to Claudia. The conversation between Abby and Brene was the perfect distraction for Claudia as she entered the second mile of her run.

She suddenly stopped. *WTF?!* she thought as she tapped the screen to rewind the conversation between Abby and Brene. Something Claudia just heard had struck a chord.

Abby was talking about a concept she called "Lead from the Bench." She told the story of the last year she played with Team USA in 2015 at the World Cup in Canada. She shared that she was thirty-five years old at this time, which is on the upper end of the age bracket for a professional athlete. She admitted that she was now older and slower, and that this tournament was one of the longer tournaments the team plays in. Halfway through the tournament, the coaching staff sat her down and explained how they wanted to make sure at the end of the tournament that she was on the field so she could experience the end of the last game. They wanted this for Abby because this would be her last World Cup experience. This meant that Abby would now be starting the following games on the bench.

She went on to talk about how this made her feel and how devastated she was when she went back to her hotel that day. Abby had a difficult time wrapping her head around the concept and accepting her fate for the rest of the games. As the leading goal scorer of the world and having played every minute of every world championship her team was in, she just couldn't accept the fact that she would no longer be starting on the field. She used words like *embarrassed* and talked about how she didn't know how she would face the world. *Holy crap*, Claudia thought as she stood on the running path and immediately connected with the feelings that Abby was describing. Devastation and embarrassment were two emotions that she was definitely experiencing. She was anxious to hear more.

Abby then said something that lit a fire in Claudia's soul. She talked about the moment in her hotel room and how she was processing everything when she realized something, and she asked herself, *Am I going to be a good teammate and sit on the bench and cheer my team on, or am I going to live inside of my ego and be a bad teammate and pout and try to show the world that I was good enough, that I should be a starter?*

Claudia walked over to a nearby park bench, slowly sat down, and hit pause on the podcast. She couldn't believe the peaceful feeling that was starting to wash over her. As she sat on the bench, she finally realized why the vote by the board had upset her so much. *That's it; that's been my problem. Jesus, it's been my ego! My big, fat, inflated ego.* Claudia looked down at her phone and hit play, anxious for what Abby was going to share next.

Abby continued to ooze brilliance and vulnerability as she talked about how you are allowed to be devastated and disappointed when life benches you in some way, but what you aren't allowed to do is miss your opportunity to lead. That everything she now needed to learn about leadership was, in fact, sitting right there—next to her on that bench. She closed with one last note and talked about what she did in the moments of accepting the role she was given, regardless of whether she agreed with it or not. She shared how supporting the decision the coaches had made to start her on the bench gave the rest of the team the confidence to go out and play their best. Her personal acceptance of the situation was also acceptance of them and demonstrated her confidence in them. "It's what being a good team player, and strong leader is all about," Claudia heard Abby say.

Claudia had found the root of her pain. Abby's story made her realize that she truly didn't want the role of Board President, but rather, the title and prestige that came with it. She recalled working on her presentation and thinking, *Can you really be effective and give this role what it needs? Your plate is so full, and the girls want to play sports and try ballet.* She took her headphones out and realized that she had not been honest with herself. She knew that her ego was leading her desire to be board president. She recalled how she felt the past week, whether she was working on the presentation or just talking to Patrick while she practiced. There was always something there in her heart that felt a bit heavy, anxious, and complex. At times, preparing for the presentation even felt forced. But now, she felt light, energized, happy, and excited that the next decision she was going to make was easy.

She had busted through her ego and was ready to take action. She checked her watch and realized she had been sitting on the bench longer than she thought. *Good God, the girl's bus will be here in ten minutes!* Standing up, she did a quick sprint home.

"Hello! Where is everyone?" Patrick shouted as he walked in the door. He walked towards the kitchen and saw that the table was set and had a fresh bouquet of flowers in the middle with their special occasion, linen napkins carefully placed next to each plate. With still no evidence of his family, he walked towards the back door and opened the slider to the patio where he found everyone giggling and chasing bubbles.

"Hi, honey!" Claudia exclaimed as she stood up and walked over to give him a kiss.

"Well, hello!" he said as he kissed and hugged her back. "This is an awesome setup to come home to. I love the happy energy."

"That's the only way to roll, my dear!" Claudia enthusiastically responded while dipping a plastic wand into the bubble mix.

"So...you obviously and awesomely turned a corner today – what happened?" Patrick sat down on the end of a chaise lounge on the patio, and Claudia proceeded to share the epiphany she had during her run. Patrick was wowed and impressed. "Holy cow, Clauds, that is a very cool story." She was full of smiles, and Patrick could tell her head was now in a healthy place.

"Ready for dinner? I baked something special for dessert!"

That night, after the girls went to bed, Claudia grabbed her phone to check the time. "Hmmm, I wonder if it's too late?" she asked herself as she contemplated texting Christine. She was still feeling great about the decision she had made and did not want to wait until the following week to share this with Christine. With a tap of her finger, she was now scrolling and looking for Christine's number.

> *Hi Christine – I hope it's not too late to send you this. I've put more thought into our conversation and would love to talk with you at your first opportunity. No need to wait until next week. Can you let me know when you have time for a coffee? Thx, Claudia*

OK, now we wait, Claudia thought to herself. She knew she had a few emails to send before turning in, and was still feeling energized with the day's events. She started jotting down new ideas around the programming Christine had discussed during her speech. A few moments later, her phone buzzed.

> *Hi Claudia! I'm a night owl – it's never too late to message me. I'm free tomorrow morning until 11:30. Would you be interested in meeting at Maggie's Diner around 9 or 10?*

With a few more taps on her phone, Claudia confirmed breakfast at ten the following morning. *OK, time for bed; the emails can wait,* she thought to herself as she shut the lights off in the kitchen and walked upstairs.

The following morning, the smell of fresh coffee filled the air as Claudia sat in a booth near the window. She could see Christine walking in the door and quickly raised her hand to grab her attention. As Christine approached the booth, she had a big smile on her face and a binder under her arm. "Good morning!" she said enthusiastically.

Claudia stood up and put out her arms to give Christine a hug. "Good morning, Madam President," she replied and sat back down. The waiter quickly dashed over to the table with a full pot of coffee.

"Ladies?" he asked, holding up the pot.

"Yes! Thank you," Christine replied, settling into the booth. "I was surprised to hear from you so soon. I want you to know that I truly understand everything you're juggling while you try to find time for yourself." Claudia was nodding her head. "Listen, I'd like to jump right in and talk about the position of the committee lead that we discussed yesterday."

"I respect that, Christine, and believe that's why we're going to get along very well." Claudia was quick to reply, "My decision is backed by a long and interesting story that I would love to share with you sometime - however, because I'm so excited, I wanted to tell you before next week that I would love to work with you on the board and take the committee leadership role."

Christine had a huge smile as she clapped her hands together. "That's outstanding, Claudia; you made my day."

"Do you need creamer, miss?" The waiter asked her as he filled her mug.

"No, thank you, I'm fine," Christine replied as she picked up the mug and held it for a toast. "To doing amazing things together," she cheered, and the two tapped their mugs. Christine took a sip of the warm brew and broke out her binder. "I'm sensitive to your time, Claudia, but I wanted to share a few of my initial ideas based on both of our presentations."

"Sounds great; I'm all ears." Christine pulled out a page that had a list of program names on it. She spent a few minutes reviewing each one, providing a quick description when she stopped and paused on the last line.

"Ready to order, ladies?" she heard as she turned to see their attentive waiter standing at the end of the table.

"I'm sorry, can you give us a few minutes, please?" Claudia responded and went back to the list. "OK, remember, this is a list of new ideas that I have. Some may stick, and some won't. However, this one is something I believe makes sense and would like to dive into." Claudia leaned on the table and saw Christine's finger pointing at a bullet that said *Building Your Personal Board of Directors*.

"That's interesting; what does it mean?" Christine described a concept she was introduced to at a recent women's leadership conference.

"You essentially build and are the chairman of your own board of directors, which is a group of people that you identify using some simple criteria. These people are there to support your personal and professional growth. When I think about the residents at Campbell House, I wonder about the job and skills programming we offer them and how we can enrich it. Let's face it, at the end of the day, who you know does make a difference, and I'd love to help the people who go through our program develop a network and build their own personal board that can support them going forward."

"I love it!" Claudia replied. "This entire concept makes

perfect sense. It's unique and easy to understand. How do we get started?"

"The class I took was delivered by a high-energy woman named Madeline Kaye. It's her original concept and something that she delivers to corporations and also online. I would love to bring her on as a committee lead and have you as the chair of the Campbell House committees, have this be our first project."

"Sounds great; I can't wait to meet her. This is exciting, Christine, something the board will embrace." Christine was thrilled about how easily they were connecting and was especially appreciative of Claudia's enthusiasm.

"OK, awesome. Let me send her an email right now and see when she would be available to meet with us. She's already aware that I want to introduce this idea at Campbell House. She's a force of nature and also one of my close friends. I told her that I wanted to start the conversation with you and make sure you liked the concept." Christine grabbed her phone and started typing away.

Hey Maddie! I wanted to reach out and follow up on our conversation. As you know, I'm a huge fan of your program and was recently appointed President of the Campbell House board. My first initiative is to introduce your program and the importance of building your network, and I would love to talk with you about bringing the program into the Campbell House agenda. Can you let me know when you would be free next week to meet with me and our awesome Program Committee Lead, Claudia Nichols? She's the CHRO at The Hemisphere Group and a tenured board member at Campbell House.

Look forward to hearing from you soon.

xoxo

"Excuse me, ladies, I don't mean to interrupt but are you ready to order?" The waiter asked.

"Gosh, we haven't even looked at the menu. I just need a moment," Christine responded.

Claudia flipped over her menu, "I usually get the same thing anyway; everything is excellent here. I'm going to indulge and get the bacon waffles."

"Dang, that sounds great, but I'm thinking savory," Christine thought. "Hmmm...sweet or savory?"

"Why don't you order something savory, and we'll split each dish – best of both worlds?" Claudia suggested.

"Great thinking! Look at us, already successfully collaborating!"

6

Personal Board of Directors

Madeline

God, I'm starving, Madeline thought to herself as she searched for a seat at the bar at her favorite restaurant, Robertos Farm Italianate. It was one of the best farm-to-table restaurants in the city, and it had amazing pizza and other fresh delights. The biggest bonus was that it was within walking distance from her condo. Robertos was a familiar destination that she considered her happy place every time she returned from a trip, especially when she had been on the road for an extended period of time. It was 3:00 on a Friday afternoon as she had just flown in from London, where she delivered the last workshop of her four-part series around Building your Personal Board of Directors.

"No suitcase this time?" The bartender asked.

"Nope, I was able to hold off my hunger long enough to toss my suitcase through the door at home and then head over here to see you, David. What's the new drink special?" she asked.

"Nelson's Green, it's a super smooth Tennessee whiskey

that's our pour of the month."

"Sounds great, my friend!" Madeline responded as she settled into the back of her leather bar stool.

Madeline Kaye was an entrepreneur. For most of her life, her career was spent in corporate America. Her resume included journeys spanning account and project management, marketing and partnerships, and most recently, global alliance programming. A fierce advocate for elevating the next generation of female leaders, especially when it came to jobs in male-dominated industries, she had a successful track record of working in the areas of finance and technology. Madeline's experience provided her with a large inventory of stories that told tales of women being overlooked for promotions, denied raises, or getting paid less than their male peers. There were also stories that included verbal and emotional abuse at work and in one instance, assault as one of the male managers she worked for tried to force himself on a female co-worker in a parking lot after a colleague's birthday party. Her energy was high and her passion rich regarding empowering women and ensuring they felt like they had options when it came to growing their careers, building their networks, and becoming financially independent.

Madeline was single with two broken engagements in her past. Every time she wanted to take a career risk or make a giant leap, her partner failed to support her, which was something she refused to compromise on. Her life was lonely at times, but she focused on looking forward, and with great friends and a strong network where she could always find the support, advice, and companionship she needed.

After a thirty-year adventure with corporate life, she hit a point where she had saved enough money and was ready to start her own company. She delivered in-person and online courses focused on helping people feel empowered and advance their careers by building stronger networks. Her online courses and speaking opportunities were starting to take off, which was something she was very proud of.

"Here you go, Maddie," she heard David say as he placed a beautiful, crystal rock glass that held a generous pour of whiskey in front of her.

"You're the best; can I have a water, and an order of the kale chopped salad with grilled chicken?" she asked as she pulled out her laptop.

Time to see what I've missed, she thought to herself as she scrolled through the list of new emails in her inbox. There was a solid inventory of the usual suspects, including tons of spam from unknown companies who had sucked her email address into their database and were asking for time on her calendar. She clicked and pressed the Shift key to highlight a group of unwanted messages that would go unread. "Dear Sir," was the last thing she saw in the preview window before hitting the delete key. *How rude!* she thought to herself when she realized that her scrolling had included one email too many. "Wait! Christine!!" she said out loud as she hit the undo button, inviting the sea of useless emails back to her inbox.

She immediately located the note from Christine and with a click of her mouse, was looking at something that sang to her soul. Reading Christine's message, she could feel her jet-lagged body lighten up. Her flight home from London found her journaling about how she could expand her reach and do more work with non-profits. She loved and respected Christine as she always admired her ability to lead with grace and calm. Madeline had often referred to Christine as the "Buddha Boss," as she had worked with Christine in the last two corporate jobs she held and always admired her management style. She quickly hit reply to let her friend know how interested she was in talking with her.

> OMG Christine! You have no idea how great it is to hear from you. I miss you!
>
> Congrats on the role, The Campbell House board sounds like a great group of people. I hope they realize how lucky they are to have you as a member of their team. I would love to meet Claudia and talk with you both about applying my program at Campbell House. I just returned from an overseas trip that had me thinking a TON about how I can expand my reach in the non-profit space and pay it forward more, so your timing couldn't be better.
>
> Claudia sounds amazing, and I can't wait to meet her. Let me know when you both are free—and FYI, breakfast is on me at Maggie's.
>
> Hugs,
>
> Mads

"Here you go, my friend," she heard David say as he placed one of her favorite dishes in front of her.

Madeline finished the last drops of her whiskey and, as she placed her glass on the bar, replied, "Perfect, as always, David, thank you. Now, how about a glass of Sauvignon Blanc to complete this picture?" David gave her a nod and turned to reach for a white wine glass from the shelf behind him. She watched David and took a moment to appreciate where she was at, the success of her trip and the excitement, thrill, and appreciation she felt for the email she had just received. She was happy about the life she had built for herself and was anxious to share her blessings with the rest of the world.

"How is everything?" he asked as she watched him fill her glass with chilled white wine.

Madeline nodded and gave him a thumbs up as her mouth was full of kale and flavors of homemade poppyseed dressing. Yep, life is good she thought to herself as she finished her meal.

Her short walk back to her condo had her thinking about what she had to do over the weekend. *Laundry, grocery shopping, as I don't have a crumb of anything edible in my pantry, complete my invoicing* were to-do's she added to her list as she enjoyed her stroll home. She walked in the door and dropped her keys on the counter in the kitchen, then moved towards her home office to unload her backpack and computer.

As she left her office on a mission to enjoy one more glass of wine before bed, she paused. She glanced at her suitcase in the hallway and then turned to her master bedroom, where she could see her soaker tub. *Hmmm—wine and unpack or wine and a bubble bath?* she asked herself.

A few minutes later, the sound of the running water as she uncorked a bottle of chardonnay confirmed the winner. Settling into the tub, her mind was a flurry of ideas about how she would align her program with the needs of the women at Campbell House. *How do we nail this and identify the next steps? How can I scale and support a program at a non-profit?* She silently asked herself while taking a sip of the buttery chardonnay. As she slipped deeper into the water, she could feel a smile spread across her face as she gave thanks for what her life had become.

The following Tuesday, Madeline was driving to Maggie's Diner, hoping she would get there early. She walked in the door and instantly made eye contact with Maggie. "Hi ya, stranger!" Maggie exclaimed as she walked over to give Madeline a hug.

"I just got back from a long trip," Madeline replied. "With all my traveling, I gotta to tell ya, I have been longing for your bacon waffles!"

Maggie grinned and nodded her head as she reached for menus. "How many this morning?" she asked, to which Madeline replied, "three, please."

As the two women walked towards a booth in the far corner of the restaurant, Madeline heard a shout from behind. "Maaa-dee!" She turned around to see Christine with her arms wide open and a giant grin on her face.

"Hey, lady!" she responded and raced back to where Christine was standing. The two women embraced, and upon releasing the lock on her friend, Madeline saw a woman standing a few feet behind Christine. The woman extended her hand and said,

"Hello, I'm Claudia."

"So nice to meet you," Madeline said and walked toward Claudia with her arms wide open. "I'm a hugger," she said, as she smiled and gave Claudia a gentle hug.

After the ladies settled into the booth, Maggie stood at attention at the end of the table, "Who would like to start with coffee?" she asked. All three women raised their hands.

"Thank you so much for meeting us, Maddie, and considering helping us build out a networking program," Christine began.

"There's nothing to consider, Christine. I'm in, committed, and eager to learn more."

Christine and Claudia looked at each other and smiled. Christine stretched her hand across the table and landed it on top of Madeline's arm. "This is the opportunity we had always talked about, Maddie," she said, leaning onto the table. Claudia quickly looked at Christine as she sat back up in the booth. "Maddie and I crossed paths in corporate America a number of years ago and often talked about how we wanted to start a non-profit or launch a foundation together." Claudia nodded.

Madeline then placed both hands on the table and said, "OK, lay it on me!"

Christine smiled and reached for her binder that contained data sheets and demographic charts about the residents of Campbell House. "I'd like to start with what 'good' looks like once we launch the program. You know, define success first." She then proceeded to talk about the mission of Campbell House and her vision around expanding their job placement and training opportunities with programming focused on growing your professional network. "What do you think?" Christine asked.

"What do I always say?" Madeline replied. "Finish the sentence. Your network is..."

Christine smiled and responded, "your net worth—of course!"

Madeline continued to listen to Christine and Claudia, and was getting excited about ways to get started. "What do you think your biggest challenge will be, both before and after we roll out the program?" she asked.

"Confidence," Claudia replied.

"Really?" Madeline questioned. "You mean from the board or from the residents?"

"Not confidence in the program Madeline, but the confidence of the women that will be in your program," said Claudia. Madeline nodded to confirm she understood.

Claudia continued. "Most of these women are so down on themselves and feel broken when they come to us. It's hard for them to escape the hopelessness and heartbreak they've been living with for so long. We realize this program won't resonate with everyone, but for those residents that are committed to changing their circumstances and creating a future for themselves, we'd love to offer them something that includes training and job placement opportunities. We've never done anything like this at Campbell House before, and the board is very excited to see what we can do. These people have also been out of the workforce for a while and have not been in a position to create, let alone maintain a professional network. You know, I've been in HR for over seventeen years and know that regardless of the path you take, building your network also builds your confidence. The security and peace of mind when you know you have a team of people you can count on for advice and support is invaluable. Apologies, I don't mean to rant on about this—it just happens to be something that I'm personally very passionate about."

Claudia's talk track was interrupted by the sound of a coffee pot being placed on the table, "Excuse me, ladies, just checking in—would you like some more coffee, or are you ready to order?" Maggie asked as she flipped the page on her notepad, waiting to hear what the group's reply would be.

"I'm ready!" Madeline exclaimed. "Bacon waffles with a side of fruit, please."

"I'll take the special," Claudia replied.

"Chilaquiles it is!" Maggie noted.

Christine hemmed and hawed a bit, "Sorry folks, I wasn't ready...what if I nibble off each of your plates and order two eggs, scrambled?"

"Works for us!" Madeline and Claudia replied in unison.

"OK, thank you—now back to it, ladies!" Maggie commanded as she waved her pen and stepped away from the table.

Almost an hour later, the three women were signing their checks and slipping their credit cards back into their wallets. "This was really amazing and inspirational, and I want you both to know that I can't wait to help you drive this forward," Madeline shared as she stood up from the booth.

"Love you. Maddie," Christine replied as she leaned in for a hug.

"Love you back."

"It was really great meeting you, Maddie," Claudia echoed. "I look forward to working with you."

Madeline looked down at her watch, "Shit! Sorry ladies, I'm five minutes behind and don't want to be late for my next meeting—it's a new customer pitch at one of the biggest Fortune 500 organizations I've ever met with; I need to bolt."

Claudia paused, "I know you're late, and I don't want to keep you, but I had no idea that you serviced large corporations. I'm the CHRO of The Hemisphere Group, and I would love to talk with you more about how we could apply your networking principles at my company." Madeline felt her heart leap. The Hemisphere Group was one of the largest insurance companies in the country, and now she had a direct way in through the Chief Human Resources Officer.

"That would be great, and thank you. I'll send you an email, and I'll find a time when we can meet."

"Awesome," Claudia replied as the two shared a hug before heading to the door. "Good luck with your meeting!"

Later that afternoon, Madeline was giddy about the type of day she was having. Pulling out of the parking lot from where she had delivered one of the biggest presentations of her career, she felt strong and confident because she knew the meeting went well. There were high levels of interest in what she had to say and lots of positive buying questions.

Madeline was full of gratitude. She understood the power behind the statement that your network is your net worth and incorporated it into her daily routine. *You never know where that next conversation will lead you and who you will meet as you follow your path*, she thought to herself as she reflected on the conversation with Claudia at breakfast. She also knew that networks weren't a one-way street, as a healthy network comes from providing as much if not more value to the people you know vs. the benefits you gain from knowing them.

One of her favorite principles that she incorporated into her program was, that the time to reach out to your network is not when you need something. This got her thinking about what she could bring to Claudia. *Maybe I can do some research on her career to understand her background and what she prioritizes. She's obviously passionate about giving back, but what else can I bring to the table to help her on the professional front? I'll talk to Christine and get a better profile of her*, Madeline thought to herself. *Who in my network can I introduce her to that she would find valuable?*

Madeline kept thinking as she continued her drive home. She then realized she was going to hit the start of rush hour and considered a different plan. *Hmmm – there's a coffee shop at this exit where I can kill some time and actually be productive as I know once I get home after fighting this traffic, I won't be motivated to do anything but grab some cheese and crackers and plop myself down on the couch.* She took the next exit and quickly landed in a Starbucks parking lot.

Walking into the coffee shop, Madeline was welcomed by the smell of fresh ground coffee, which brought a small smile to her face. As she stood in line, she heard the man in front of her order a large coffee with extra Splenda. Her memory rewound to her ten-year-old self, standing in the kitchen in the house where she grew up. She could hear the sound of the

Mr. Coffee pot lift from the coffee maker as her mom poured the warm black liquid into a mug she had given her for Mother's Day that had painted hearts on it. Next came the gentle sound of thin paper ripping as her mom would stir in three packages of Sweet & Low carefully into her drink. Sitting at the table each morning, eating her Frosted Flakes before they turned soggy, Madeline recalled the list of questions about her lunch and homework her mom would run through before school.

Her journey back to her childhood was interrupted by a young man behind the counter, "Hello, Ma'am—are you ready to order?" he asked.

"Jeez, I'm sorry. I spaced out there for a moment; I guess I need a cup of coffee more than I realized to wake myself up! Grande latte, please."

"No problem," he replied. "What's your name?"

"Maddie," she said as she walked towards a small table in the corner to get comfortable. Pulling out her laptop, memories of her mom sitting at the kitchen table were still vivid. Growing up, she had watched her mom struggle as her dad was an alcoholic and would binge drink on the weekends. She knew from a young age that her mom wanted a different life. She and her brothers always felt loved and were well taken care of, but her mom was often depressed and fought about money with her father, often. Her mom had dropped out of high school to support her grandmother after her grandfather passed away and never went back. A hard worker, she always had one or two part-time jobs to ensure she had her own spending money and to avoid asking

Madeline's father for anything. *She was stuck; she had friends but no one who really knew how to help her*, Madeline thought to herself. While Madeline's program helped men and women at various stages of their careers grow their network, deep down she knew her drive to help others came from her mom. Madeline wished she could have found a way to help build her mom's confidence and, ultimately, to live the life she really wanted. It had been fifteen years since her mom had lost her battle with cancer, and the hole this left in Madeline's heart was still there.

"Miss, excuse me—Maddie, right?" she heard a voice say as she looked up, startled by the young man who had taken her coffee order and now stood next to her table. "Your latte."

"Oh man, I am so sorry. I didn't hear you call my name."

"No worries, enjoy your drink," he said as he walked back to the counter. The creaminess of the warm latte was extremely satisfying as she removed the plastic lid and took her first sip from the paper cup.

OK, let's update the list! was the first thing she thought and, with a few clicks of her mouse, launched her CRM software. This was a practice Madeline was religious about at the end of every workday, and sometimes on the weekend. She would think about the people she had met that day and enter their contact information into her contact management software, along with a task to follow-up with them within the next seven days. A big proponent of building a strong network, she practiced what she preached and made sure that she constantly reached out to her network to share an article or see where she could help. Madeline was always thinking about what kind of value she could offer and who in her current network she could introduce each contact to.

She thought about her first meeting of the day with Claudia. As she entered Claudia's details, she thought about the promise of the relationship as she was thrilled about her being a potential new client but was more excited about partnering with her at Campbell House. *It's really awesome when you can marry your personal passions with your day job.* For the next ninety minutes, Madeline worked through her contact list, follow-up tasks, and email cleanup. She leaned back in her chair and noticed the time on her screen. *Dang, time flew—there should be no traffic now*, she thought as she gathered her trash and packed her laptop for the drive home.

Grabbing her phone to verify the traffic situation, she saw a call from Christine pop up on her screen. "Hey, you! Miss me already?"

"Of course!" Christine quickly replied. "Do you have a minute, Maddie? I have a big ask."

"Hit me; what's up?"

"Well, I know it's totally last minute, and well, wait. First, I want to thank you for the great conversation and willingness to support Claudia and I at breakfast today."

Madeline paused just before getting to her car, "Christine, come on—no need to layer on this sweetness. We're sisters, and I couldn't be more excited about helping you and the residents at Campbell House. Just tell me what you need."

"You're right, Maddie, I'm sorry. We are sisters, and I want to make sure you never feel like I'm taking you for granted. Here's the deal ..."

As Madeline got into her car, the call switched to Bluetooth, and she heard Christine say, "... so would tomorrow work for you, the afternoon would be preferable."

"I'm sorry, Christine, you flipped to Bluetooth as I was getting in the car and I'm pretty sure I missed the big ask."

"No problem, let me start over and provide some more detail. Today after breakfast, I had my weekly call with the chairman of our board. I told him about your program and your willingness to help us, and he's pretty pumped. I mean, Max is a 'get it done' kind of guy, and with that comes high levels of energy, but this is the first time I've seen him so enthusiastic about a new initiative. We have an aggressive timeline, and he's going on vacation in two days, so I was wondering if you are available to come to the center and meet with us, including Claudia, to present your program and recommend some next steps before Max goes on vacation. I know you're going to work on a special version of the program just for the Campbell House residents, and thought it would be best if Max heard directly from you what that process is going to be so we can support you in the best way possible."

Madeline quickly responded, "That's an easy one, Christine; it just so happens I have some time tomorrow afternoon. What were you thinking?"

"How does 3:00-4:00 work for you?" Christine replied.

"You got it, sister!" Madeline shouted.

She heard Christine sigh and knew she was smiling, "This is awesome, Maddie, I can't wait to get started."

As Madeline drove down the empty freeway and headed into the city, she started to think about the parts of her program that would resonate best with the residents of Campbell House. She knew she had to change her current track of "building a personal board of directors", as the women at Campbell House most likely had no network to use. They were starting from scratch. She did want to make sure that building a personal board was a long-term goal and wanted them to understand the positive impact this would have on their careers and even life. The challenge of a non-corporate audience was a bit daunting for her, but the energy she felt quickly diluted her anxiety and was something she had never felt before. She knew this project would be great, and working with Christine and Claudia would be awesome, but there was something else that was pushing her to do this.

She didn't know what it was, but she knew that it was positive and made her heart light up. As she pulled into her parking garage, she said a short prayer to trust her instincts and bring her best to the meeting tomorrow afternoon.

That night, Madeline tossed and turned. She knew her meeting with Christine the next day was a low-pressure event, but there was something still nagging her that she could not identify. The last thing she remembered was looking at her phone and seeing a 4:17 AM time stamp. Next thing she knew, the alarm was actually waking her up at 6:00 am! "Ugh"... she rolled over and was dreading how she would look, as she feared how dark and deep the bags under her eyes would be due to her lack of quality sleep.

She pulled herself out of bed and walked into the kitchen. Grabbing the bag of coffee beans she felt herself slowly wake up. Madeline loved what she did and usually popped out of bed, ready to roll every day. But last night's distractions and the unique energy pull she felt around this opportunity at Campbell House had her curious and intrigued. *There's something different about this* she thought as she made sure the filter was evenly placed in the coffee maker. She didn't know what it was, but she couldn't shake the feeling that something bigger than her presentation was going to take place that day.

Pulling into the parking lot of Campbell House, Madeline could feel herself getting excited as her confidence was building around her ideas for a custom version of her program. "Hey, you!" she heard as she was getting out of her car and pulling out her briefcase. She turned to see Christine walking toward her. "Early as usual," she shouted.

The two met and shared a long hug before heading into the building. "This is not a big, formal thing," Christine said as she opened the door for Madeline to walk in.

"I know, I'm chill. It's all about first impressions, and I just want to show up strong and positive today." The women walked into the main conference room, where they were greeted by Claudia and Max.

"Madeline, I assume," Max said as he walked toward her with his hand extended.

"So nice to meet you, Max. I've heard amazing things about Campbell House and what your board is hoping to accomplish. I'm grateful to be part of this conversation."

For the next few minutes, the group settled in and took their seats around the conference room table. Madeline pulled out four sets of stapled sheets she had prepared the night before. The title page read: *Campbell Connected—Building Your Personal Board of Directors.*

Pulling a packet toward him, Max said, "I love the name."

"Thank you, I've learned that it's important to brand programs like these, even if they are internal, because it helps give the program an identity and a persona of its own," Madeline replied.

For the next twenty minutes, Madeline walked the group through the steps of the program that had been built on her own core offering, which had helped corporate employees build their personal board of directors. "I'll be honest, my biggest challenge was how to take a program that assumes its participants already have a network of some type and are actively employed and apply it to the unemployed. Before we can talk about building a personal board of directors, we need to define what a strong network is. A strong network is the bedrock for building your personal board of directors' pipeline. I realize that these folks are starting from scratch, so the first part of Campbell Connected is centered around growing and nurturing your network."

She asked everyone to turn to the next page.

Claudia was nodding her head, and Madeline paused, feeling that she wanted to say something.

"This is a great start Madeline," Claudia said. "You know, I've been a full-time professional for over twenty years, and you're expanding my understanding of what a strong

What is a Strong Network?

What it is:

- A lifelong and on-going endeavor / labor of love
- A group of people that provide you with positive energy and a strong sense of worth
- A group of people you feed by fostering connections to each other
- Something you consistently nurture and feed and grow

What it isn't:

- Friends, family and people you only have personal relationships with
- A group of people you only reach out to when you need something
- Void of people that are not where you aspire to be

network means. You're absolutely correct when you say it should not be void of people who aren't where you aspire to be. That's brilliant!"

Madeline smiled, "Thank you, Claudia, I really appreciate the input. I've had the pleasure of talking to thousands of men and women that have helped me shape this content over the years. Another important lesson I incorporate into the training is that the time to reach out to your network is not when you need something." Everyone in the room was nodding in agreement. "We talk about ways to keep your network warm and how to deliver value to others on a regular basis."

"Before I continue, I want to check in with you all and see if I'm on track with the level of detail for the women here, as I'm pretty excited to move onto the next page."

Max spoke up, "I appreciate that Madeline, as we know it might be tricky for our residents to connect to some of the concepts here. We know that not every resident will be a good candidate for this program, but there are women that were in the workforce not that long ago and just fell on hard times over the past few years. They will be some of the best people to take this training."

"That's great to hear, Max. Let's turn to the next page." The sound of papers flipping was followed by quick silence. Madeline took a long pause as she watched everyone read through the content on the next page.

Why is a Strong Network Important?

- Helps you accelerate your goals and achieve your dreams
  - o You don't have to figure everything out on your own
- A way to deliver value to others (people both in and outside your network)
  - o Making introductions and connections to others is a great way to deliver value
- A safe place for you to explore and test new ideas
  - o This is your judgement free zone
- You can turn to it for inspiration
  - o Creative things happen when you nurture, feed and grow your network
- It's a conduit for bigger things
  - o Will support your career advancement, personal development and goal achievement

---

"So true, Madeline," Christine volunteered. "This slide is great and makes me excited for what's next."

"If our most trusted group looks and sounds like us, they will have limits on how far they can help us move forward."

"I appreciate that. It's important to remember that having a diverse network ensures you are gaining insight from people with different perspectives and experiences. This type of insight is invaluable when it comes to defining your career path, regardless of whether you're just starting out or have been employed forever." The nonverbal affirmations from the room told Madeline that she was on the right track.

Madeline went on to talk about the initial process of establishing goals and intentions for yourself and emphasized the importance of these two items serving as a North Star when it's time to identify what you want to talk to your network about.

Setting your goals and intentions

- Your goal is what you want to achieve:
  "I want to get a full-time job doing social media"

- Your intention is you want and plan to do – it's the process you through until you get to want you want to achieve:
  "I will follow social media influencers that I want to mirror"
  "I will learn about a new social media platform each week"
  "I will stay open minded to fresh ideas about social media promotion"

1. Write it down! (Grab a journal or start a new Word document)
2. Open up!   (How will it make you feel when you reach that goal)
3. Re-visit it! (Remind / reflect on what your intentions are, update them regularly)
4. Keep it fun! (You should never feel resistance, if you do revisit your goal or intention)

"I love this and believe this will land well with our residents," Max shared.

Christine half raised her hand, "I totally agree but realize we're almost out of time. Looks like this is the last page, Mads. Is there anything else you want to cover before we bring this overview to a close?" Madeline shook her head no.

Christine continued, "I want to wrap things up by thanking my dear friend and networking thought-leader for her time and visions around what Campbell Connected could be. Gotta tell ya, I love that name!" The room shared a quick round of applause and Madeline gave them a curtsy.

"I appreciate the feedback, but there's still a ton of work to do. If you all are on board with the direction I'm taking this I would love to chat about how we roll this out and formally announce the program."

"You're reading my mind," Claudia replied. "It's been a while since we've done anything this big at Campbell House, and I want to make sure that we give this program the time and attention it deserves. With a proper launch we're likely to attract additional sponsors, which will help us manage the costs of materials and the online platform that we want to build."

"What's next?" Madeline asked quickly.

Packing up her briefcase, Christine quickly replied. "We were thinking of a large, in-person event where we would have the women of Campbell House and the general public attend and hear either a panel or speaker talk about the promise of this new program."

"Let me see if I can secure some space where we held our gala a few months ago. How many people do you think we need to accommodate?" Max asked. Everyone looked at each other in wonder.

Claudia popped up, "I would hope one hundred at a minimum; more would definitely be better. The space where the gala was held would be perfect since the parking was easy and the food was fantastic. Maybe a late afternoon or early evening program with light nibbles could work? I know we have to take a look at budgets and determine how we want to cover the costs."

"This is a great idea; let's commit to making it happen," Max responded.

Christine chimed in, "OK, let's start talking dates and meet again next week to discuss this further."

Everyone agreed and hugged before leaving the conference room. "You were awesome, my sister," Christine whispered into Madeline's ear as they finished their hug.

Madeline smiled, "I feel like this is what I should be doing right now. Thank you," she responded as she gave Christine's hand a tight squeeze.

Madeline walked in the door of her condo full of positive energy and excitement about the meeting with Christine and the team earlier that day. Entering her kitchen she placed her purse on the countertop and her briefcase on the floor. Opening the cabinet that housed her rock glasses, she selected one of her favorite crystal designs. "Nope, this is a special toast," she thought to herself and placed the glass back on the shelf, and walked towards the small bar in the corner of her dining area. She looked down at a set of beautiful antique glasses that she had received as a gift. These were her special occasion glasses, and she loved the way the silver design that was etched on the outside of the glass felt in her hand. She picked up the glass with her left hand and one of her favorite bourbons in her right. *Blanton's feel right today,* she thought to herself as she poured the brown liquid into her glass.

Walking over to her couch to wind down for the evening, she kicked off her shoes and took a sip. As she savored the taste of the bourbon, she paused. Her thoughts bounced to her mom and the programming she had discussed with the Campbell House team. *Geez, is that was she was lacking?* she thought to herself. *Mom had no one to talk to and really no idea how to ask for help.* She could feel a light layer of sadness come over her as her heart broke for her mom when she thought back to her childhood and often wondered if she was depressed. *Was she hopeless?*

Sitting up on the couch, she folded her legs to get comfortable in a cross-legged position. She took another sip from her glass that she was now holding with both hands and wondered, *This is what I'm supposed to do. Help others that don't know how to help themselves...help them feel empowered.* She could feel her soul start to smile.

She was already confident about Campbell Connected launching, but felt challenged as she thought about her mom and how she could have used a program like this. *But mom wouldn't have found my program through Campbell House because she had a home and a way to care for her family. Where could she have gone? How could something like Campbell Connected find her? She had no idea how to build a network. She needed something to give her confidence so she could explore a career. How could this program make her feel stronger...almost fearless?* She spun the glass around in her hands, mulling over the question. *What would it take to make someone like Mom feel safe and partake in something like Campbell Connected? What if there was a community of other women that were just like her that she could easily relate to? Would she have shown up?*

She reached for a coaster to set her glass down on the coffee table and bounced off the couch to head toward the kitchen, where she knew a scratch pad and pen were waiting for her. She started to write.

A community of like-minded women who are sharing the same plights.

Scared, nervous, and overwhelmed by the thought of finding a job.

Want to build a network but don't know how to start.

Help them feel empowered.

Make them fearless.

She set down the pen and reached for her phone. *I have to call Christine; I need to hash this out. Time to reach out to my sister to polish this idea up.* As Madeline picked up her phone to dial her friend, the phrase *my fearless sister* came to mind. As she scrolled to Christine's name on the screen and said out loud, "OMG, of course!" She listened to Christine's phone ring, anxious for her to pick up.

"Hey, you!" Christine enthusiastically answered.

"Sorry, just a sec," Madeline replied as she placed the phone between her ear and shoulder, freeing up her hand. She grabbed the pen and wrote *Fearless Sisters* on the scratch pad and drew a big circle around the words. "Hey, sorry about that, Christine. Got a minute? I'd love to run an idea past you."

The following week Madeline was pulling into the parking lot of Campbell House, ready for her next meeting with Claudia and the team. Since their last meeting, she had been somewhat consumed with her thoughts around Campbell Connected in a very positive way. She felt good about how she had reworked her Personal Board of Directors program to align with the needs of the women at Campbell House. She was also excited about the outline she had built to support a version of the program for Fearless Sisters, which was a new program she was going to roll out on her own. It had been a good week of progress for Madeline on many fronts, and she was more excited than ever about rolling up her sleeves and getting started.

Walking towards the front door, she caught up with Max, who held it open for her. "Good morning, Madeline," he said as he waited for her to walk through.

"Thank you, Max, and good morning to you as well." The two entered the conference room where they were greeted by Claudia and Christine, who had been meeting on other board matters.

"Hello!" Claudia shouted, welcoming Max and Madeline.

"Hi, ladies," Madeline replied. "Are you ready to get started? I'm pretty excited about the updates I've made and would love to discuss the launch event before I leave."

"Love the energy, Mads," Christine replied. "We're ready."

Madeline didn't waste any time diving in. "I've really enjoyed editing my program to create something that will resonate with the women of Campbell House. I specifically targeted people who are just starting or hitting re-set on their career journey." She flipped the display from her laptop to a screen at the front of the room. As she walked toward the screen, she explained what the rest of the room had started to read. "'Campbell Connected – A Field Guide to Building Your Personal Board of Directors'. I liked the reference to field guides as I want the program to feel like a tool that the women refer to and reuse as they start their journey. Field guides are things people actually take into the field for reference, so my hope is that this program ends up being something they continually turn to for support and insight, as compared to attending a one-and-done training class."

Everyone in the room was nodding; Madeline continued and advanced to the next slide. "I want to get ahead of questions they might be asking themselves to ensure they feel connected to the content." She pointed to the screen and started to review the questions on the slide.

- Why do I need a Personal Board of Directors?
- Who should be on my board, and how do I find them?
- What do I do with my board once I identify them?

Claudia raised her hand to politely interrupt. "Madeline, I think this is perfect, and to be honest, I want the answers to these questions as well."

"I'm happy to hear that Claudia, because these questions will serve as the key pillars of the program. I've created reference notes and worksheets that will serve as the main content of the program and will be organized around three questions. I'd like to use these questions to introduce the program at our launch event to give the audience a small taste of what they will learn." Madeline advanced through her remaining slides and reviewed everything from the program worksheets and exercises to the timeline and other resources she would use to roll the program out.

"OK, that's everything I have right now," she said as she clicked to her last slide. "Time to talk about the actual launch event with the time we have left."

"I totally agree and really love what you have done. Every time we meet, I personally learn something about growing and managing my own network, which is very cool." Claudia replied. "I had some thoughts on the agenda of the event, if you're finished, Madeline." Madeline nodded. Claudia rested her arms on the table and leaned in a bit further. "Some of the best events I've attended have involved multiple people sharing stories and lessons learned."

"Kind of like a panel?" Christine asked.

"Yes, but what I was thinking was in lieu of a standard panel event, we could have a set of lightning talks and then follow with a Q&A session afterwards."

"What's a lightning talk?" Max asked.

"It's a quick presentation like five to seven minutes on a specific topic. It's a pretty neat way to share different stories and perspectives that are connected with a single theme."

"I love it!" Madeline replied. "What about themes like Launching my Career...The Power of my Network or My Best Lessons Learned...or something close to that; they will line up with the announcement of the Personal Board of Directors program, and its field guide pillars. Just riffing here and having some fun." The energy in the room was positive and continued to build as the team talked through what the agenda would look like.

"OK, now for the tricky part," Christine started. "How do we identify our speakers and panelists?" The group paused for a moment, unsure of where to start.

Claudia stood up and walked over to the whiteboard. "Think of our mission and the goal of the event. Now, take a deep breath and tell me the name of the first person that comes to mind".

After a few moments, Max replied, "Colleen Warner. She's the Director of Social Services for Campbell House and was just telling me about this interesting exercise she just took her team through. Maybe she can turn that into a lightning talk?" Claudia wrote her name on the board with "Team Exercise" right next to it.

"I love the idea of having someone that the residents are familiar with; everyone really loves Colleen. Didn't she just add a lawyer to her team that had taken a career break or something? I thought I remember hearing about that. I think a return to the workforce story would be interesting and relatable for our audience too."

"Yeah...it's a unique name, I think it's Bryn, but I don't know her last name. Let's check with Colleen," Max responded. Claudia wrote Bryn and "Return to Work" on the board.

"What about someone from our volunteer team? I know we have a few women that have just launched their own businesses; that could be another angle." Christine added.

"I love that," Claudia replied as she wrote Volunteer and "Launch own Business" on the board. "And let's not forget our closer," Claudia added, and wrote Madeline Kaye and "Personal Board of Directors" on the whiteboard. "This is a great start. Now to fill in the gaps with a moderator and logistics."

Max heard his phone buzz and picked it up to answer the incoming call. "Excuse me, ladies, but this might be our last logistical detail. Hello, this is Max," the room heard him answer. "That's great to hear; thank you so much. You can send the contract over today, and thank you again for supporting Campbell House." Setting his phone on the table, he said, "Well, our venue and date were just confirmed! We were able to secure the same spot where we had the gala." The room cheered and high-fived each other.

"Alright, it's time to really roll up our sleeves," Claudia announced. I'll reach out to Colleen and get going on securing our speakers. Christine, can you start the process we followed for the gala to confirm logistics and seating?" Christine gave a thumbs up. "And let's keep this meeting on the calendar each week for the three of us to connect. Time to change some lives, team!"

7

Bringing It All Together

"Wow! I love this idea; thank you so much for reaching out," Bryn exclaimed as she multi-tasked packing lunchboxes, filling her coffee thermos, and talking to Colleen. "A program to help the women of Campbell prepare for the workforce and learn how to build and use a network is brilliant. Listen, I'm honored to tell my story about how I pivoted from corporate law to working for a non-profit; I mean...you and I have had so many conversations about doing work that feeds your mind and your soul. What else can I do to help with the event? Do they need any more panelists or speakers?" Bryn paused while she zipped up her last lunch box and listened to Colleen. "OK, well, if you could ask, I would love to team up with my dear friend Claire as we worked through our transition back to the workplace together, using an exercise called the Homework Assignment. It would be great to share the lightning talk spotlight with her and have us talk about how we supported each other to define what we really wanted to do with our careers."

She listened to Colleen reply that she would check with Claudia, the woman who was managing the program agenda, and get right back to her. "OK, awesome—just let me know what she says. I'm really excited and will see you in the office this afternoon. We need to review our latest filings and orders of protection for the three women that joined last week." She heard Colleen thank her for everything that she was doing at the shelter. "Thank you, that's not necessary but appreciated. I've never been happier with the work I'm doing, and I feel like I'm the lucky one of this partnership."

Bryn hung up the phone and called to her kids. "Let's go, everyone! This show is hitting the road, and we don't want to be late!" She heard the stomping of feet running down the stairs and said a quick prayer for what her life had become as she was blessed with a healthy family and a job that she loved.

Colleen ended her call with Bryn just before pulling into the parking lot of Campbell House. She was in a great mood as her conversation with Max, Claudia, and Christine the day before was all about the event and the progress made on the workplace training program. Implementing a program like this had been a big goal of Colleen's and was something she would often write about in her Accountability Log. *It's finally becoming a reality*. The thought made her smile as she turned off her car.

Colleen ended her call with Bryn just before pulling into the parking lot of Campbell House. She was in a great mood as her conversation with Max, Claudia, and Christine the day before was all about the event and the progress made on the workplace training program. Implementing a program like this had been a big goal of Colleen's and was something she would often write about in her Accountability Log. *It's finally*

BRINGING IT ALL TOGETHER

becoming a reality. The thought made her smile as she turned off her car.

She checked her watch and realized she had just five minutes to spare before her meeting with Diana. Roger had always spoken so highly of her and the work she did with the donations program. She had been a long-time volunteer at Campbell House, and Colleen was looking forward to meeting her in person to not only express her gratitude but to learn about the business she recently launched. It helped companies build programs around hiring and providing on-the-job training assistance for people with special needs, including both mental and physical disabilities. After talking with Max about the types of people the committee needed to present a lightning talk, Diana's name quickly came to mind as she had heard that she was a top volunteer and now had a strong story to tell about how she decided to quit her full-time job and start her own company. She walked in the front door and saw a petite woman standing in the foyer. "Hello, are you Diana Fredrickson?"

"I am; pleased to finally meet you, Colleen," Diana replied and turned to shake Colleen's hand. "I've heard so many great things as Roger brags about his job here and working for you."

"He's a gem, and I can echo the positive press that he's shared with me about working with you. Thank you for stopping by - I know we could have talked on the phone, but I wanted to meet with you in person to discuss what I think could be a really great opportunity for you, especially since you've started your own business. Let's head to the conference room."

As the two walked toward the room, Diana dove right in. "It's been an exciting time for me, as I never thought about launching my own business, but then I had an inspiration followed by an opportunity to take my first step towards entrepreneurship. I leaped and have not looked back. The biggest surprise is how much this change has done for manufacturing time with my daughter. I'm a single mom and have always struggled with feelings of guilt when I would bring Linny home from school and didn't have enough time to just play with her. Now that I control my own calendar, the flexibility has been great."

Colleen grinned, "Linny?" "Oh, it's short for Caroline. It started when she was a baby and has just stuck. It really suits her."

"I love it; it's adorable as I'm sure she is as well." Diana took out her phone and pulled up pictures from the hiking adventure they had taken the previous weekend. "Those are amazing; she is really beautiful. You know, Diana, I want to talk to you about an event we're planning to announce a workplace training program we're going to launch at Campbell House. I'd love to talk more, and I think you should consider bringing Linny to the event as well."

Diana was pleasantly surprised, "Wow, I really appreciate that; what's the training program about?"

Colleen went on to discuss the details of Campbell Connected and the event, including the lighting talks and Q&A panel. "We want to showcase stories of women who have either re-entered the workforce after taking a leave of absence or have made a career pivot and have changed their jobs to something new. For your lightning talk, we'd like you to include any lessons learned, tools, or exercises you used to support your career journey."

Diana was sitting patiently, eager to respond. "There's something I did right before resigning that actually was inspired by my daughter. It's a practice that I now share with everyone I work with that is looking to make a career move." The two were now sitting at the conference room table, and Colleen put her arms on the table to lean in and hear more. "It's called The Dream Network. It's designed to help you determine your goals by dreaming big and thinking out of the box about the types of people you would like to have as part of your network. There are no limits; it could be celebrities or just personas of people you would like to meet. I like to get people excited about thinking big. It's amazing because when you take the time to think about your list, it forces you to re-visit your goals and do some soul searching."

Colleen was hooked, "I love it and want to learn more!" Diana continued to share the stories and feedback from others that she had walked through the exercise. "It actually helped open my eyes to wanting to start my own company, and I believe it led me to my first client, Claudia Nichols."

"That's right! I forgot that you and Claudia knew each other."

"I have Roger to thank for that," Diana smiled. "Part of the power of The Dream Network exercise is sharing it with others so they can extend and sometimes sponsor new connections. That's exactly what happened with Roger."

"That is extremely cool, Diana; it's going to make for a fabulous talk." The two continued to chat for another thirty minutes when Colleen glanced at her watch. "Hey, Diana, I'm sorry to do this, but I have another meeting that I have to get to. It's actually with Claudia and a few others to discuss the event. She'll be delighted to hear you're on board and will be speaking."

"Tell her I said 'hello' and let her know how grateful I am for the opportunity." The two women shared a quick hug before leaving the conference room.

Colleen was heading back to her car as her meeting was taking place at Maggie's Diner over lunch. She was excited about sharing her updates regarding the conversations with Bryn and Diana and was eager to hear from the rest of the team. Walking into the diner, Colleen was hit with the smell of coffee and fresh baked goods. *Mmmm—it's a good day to indulge*, she thought as she watched a tray loaded with a club sandwich, French fries, and what looked a mushroom Swiss burger go by. "There's my sweetheart," she heard a familiar voice say, as she turned around and saw Maggie walking up to her with open arms.

"Hi, Mom! You look nice and busy," she said, giving her mother a long hug.

"I'm very blessed and so happy to see you. How many of you today?"

"You know, I'm not sure if it's four or five. I'm meeting some board members from the shelter, and I think there's going to be someone new."

"This way," Maggie motioned, and the pair walked towards a large round table in a corner of the restaurant.

"This is perfect," Colleen replied as she pulled out a chair to get comfortable and wait for the rest of the team. A few minutes later, she saw Max, Christine, and Claudia walk through the restaurant. With a quick wave of her hand, she was able to get their attention and direct them to where she was sitting across the room. "Hi, everyone! Great to see you; take a seat!" she cheerfully greeted them.

Right behind Claudia, she saw an unfamiliar face come forward. "Hi, I'm Madeline—you must be Colleen," she heard the friendly woman say as she stuck out her hand.

"Great to meet you, Madeline; I understand you're the brains behind the workplace programming that we're going to roll out. I can't wait to hear more about it; this has been a dream of mine for a long time."

Finding her seat at the table, Madeline responded, "I'm really looking forward to getting things started; and am very proud to be associated with Campbell House. I'm super excited about the event."

"It's really magical how it's coming together," Colleen replied. "If you're ready to get started, I have some great news that I want to share with all of you. I'm happy to report that I spoke with Bryn Miles and Diana Fredrickson from your list of speakers, and they are both thrilled to be involved." Everyone clapped as Maggie walked up to the table.

"Ha! Why thank you for the applause, everyone! Now, what can I get you started with?"

The table laughed, "Mom, I'd like you to meet Max, Claudia, Christine, and Madeline. These are the people that are organizing the event that I was telling you about last week, and who are responsible for driving the workplace training program that we're going to implement."

"Mom?!" Claudia responded. "Oh my God, I've been coming here and loving this place forever and had no idea."

Maggie smiled and said, "I love that you love coming here; thank you for saying that. My Colleen is so excited about this new program, which makes me happy because the work you all do is so important. Now, what can get you all started with?"

"Your mom is a gem," Claudia said.

"She is, and her story is important as she's a Campbell House alumni."

"WHAT?!" the table exclaimed. "Yep, it was really what motivated me to go into social work. Campbell House is what helped her get back on her feet after my dad passed away. I was just a baby, and I don't remember this time at all, but she was left with nothing and learned about Campbell House through her church, " Colleen explained

"Would it be the community church at the end of this block?" Claudia asked.

"Yep, that's the one, and we still go there."

Claudia was anxious to share, "That's how my dad found out about Campbell House too."

Colleen nodded her head, "That's correct, and Roger has been one of the best hires I ever made."

"The world is a small one," Max responded as the team made room for the loaded plates of food that were slowly approaching their table.

"We still have plenty to talk through," Christine started. "Do you mind if we start while we're eating our food?" Everyone at the table shook their heads as their mouths were full. "So, Colleen, you've been able to confirm Bryn, who's going to tell her story about pivoting from corporate law to a non-profit, after taking a break to raise her family, right?"

"That's correct. However, Bryn talked about an exercise that she worked through that accelerated her decision. It's called The Homework Assignment and was something that she shared with a friend of hers that had also taken a career break and was looking to return to the workforce. They both used the exercise to explore different types of careers. Bryn asked if they could tag-team on the presentation to reinforce the power of sharing this exercise with another person. I assume this is OK, but I wanted to check with all of your first."

"I'm totally fine with it, and I think it sounds great," Claudia replied. "What's her name so we can add her to the program?"

"Claire Stanley."

"You gotta be kidding me!" Max responded. Everyone at the table was waiting to hear what was behind his reaction. "This is a small world. It has to be the same person," he said. The table was sharing confused glances with each other. "It wasn't a big deal, but we met a few months ago over a fender bender. She bumped into me at a stoplight." The table now looked shocked. "She was delightful, and everything was resolved quickly and simply. Her husband owns an insurance business and, well, it's a really small world." The team continued to enjoy their meal as they discussed the incredible connections that were being discovered.

"OK, back to the agenda," Claudia started. "We have the moms returning to the workforce as one talk. What is Diana going to talk about? She's the one who just started her own company, correct?"

"That's right," Colleen replied. "She has a really cool exercise that she wants to discuss called The Dream Network. She told me that it helped her make the decision to go out on her own. She actually credits meeting you, Claudia, as a result of sharing it with your dad."

"That's pretty awesome," Claudia replied.

"Yeah, it's about making a list of the people you would have in your network if you could ask anyone in the world. The list could include celebrities, authors, or personas —for example, someone who's a musician or started a podcast. She talks about how this exercise helps you explore and sort out what you really want to do, as your dream network becomes a reflection of your goals."

"I love it!" Exclaimed Madeline. "Her talk will set the stage for me to discuss the concept behind building your Personal Board of Directors, since it's built on growing your network. I know we want my talk to be the last one; what if we put Diana right before me?"

"This is really coming together well," Claudia replied. "OK, and Colleen, you're going to talk about the

Accountability Log exercise you and Meg have had so much success with, right?"

"That's correct. It's been such a great practice that started when Meg was in Haiti and is something that we still do weekly as it's our way to do a quick reflection on what we achieved physically and professionally the week prior, before setting new goals for the week ahead. Sharing this with a partner is the key to its success. Unfortunately, I'll be giving the talk solo as Meg lost her mom to cancer a few weeks ago and is really consumed with sorting out her personal and financial affairs."

"Yeah, I was really sad for your family to hear that," Claudia replied. "So, that makes four total talks. They are usually five minutes each so that puts us at twenty minutes total. Madeline, I would like to give you some extra time to go into to detail about Campbell Connected, but it would be nice to have a full half hour of lightning talks. Who else can we get to speak?"

"What about you?" Christine asked Claudia. Claudia glanced back at Christine with a surprised look on her face.

"Me? What would I talk about?" she asked. "Come on, Claudia; you've had an amazing career. I know there's a piece of advice you can share or a story to tell somewhere from your past. What's the last lesson that you learned?" Claudia looked at Christine, smiled then looked down at the table.

Taking a deep breath, she sat tall in her chair and said, "Lead From The Bench." The team sat around the table, waiting for the long pause to end. "It's pretty personal but is one of the best lessons I have ever learned." Claudia opened up and told the story of the board appointment and vote. She shared everything, including her frustration with Max, and questioning of Christine. "It was that podcast that changed my thinking and really my life," she continued. "The moment I realized I was allowing my ego to control my feelings, behaviors, and decisions, I broke down. I physically broke down, and after working through my emotions, I felt a sense of relief. The ego is a powerful thing and can make or break how you show up, and that doesn't just mean in your career. I have to think that the women in our program have battled their ego and lost many times. Maybe my story can help them feel normal and realize that they can be great leaders without a big title or corner office."

The table was silent. Madeline reached out to Claudia and rested her hand on her arm. "That was amazing."

"Thank you...that's the lesson that I'd like to share." Claudia felt confident about her decision as she reached for the check Maggie had just delivered to the table. "Now, to work out the details around an event title, an MC, and the introductions. Since we'll have people there that are non-residents and public supporters of Campbell House, it would be nice to do a brief overview of our history and mission." Madeline was suddenly struck with an idea.

"You're still looking for additional sponsorships, right?" she asked.

Claudia nodded, "It's always the toughest part of pulling one of these things together. We've had a few companies raise their hands, but we're still below fifty percent of our goal."

Madeline smiled, "I would love to sponsor the balance." The expressions of the faces around the table were a combination of surprise and delight. "It just hit me that this would be a great opportunity to market a new platform I'm developing. It's a digital platform called Fearless Sisters that provides tools, online courses, and programming to women who want to re-enter the workforce. My involvement with Campbell House was the inspiration for the idea, to be honest."

"Wow," Max responded. "I really love the name; it's empowering."

Claudia quickly piled on, "What if we name the event after your platform? As our top sponsor, I believe you deserve this type of benefit, I mean...if that's something you want to do. We can market the heck out of it."

"Sign me up!" Madeline exclaimed. "The Fearless Sisters Rally, Helping You Imagine Your Future and Build Your Career. I'm not sure where that just came from, but maybe something like that."

"It's perfect," Claudia replied. "That's a kickass title."

"You know what would really be cool?" Christine asked. "If we could get a resident or program graduate to deliver the overview. That would bring such a personal touch to the event." The table agreed and loved the idea.

"Here you go, my dear," Maggie said as she handed the receipt and credit card back to Claudia.

"Hey Mom, what are you doing on the 17th of July?" she heard her daughter ask.

8

The Fearless Sisters Rally

"You've got this, Mom," Maggie heard her daughter say as she placed her hands on her shoulders. "You're going to be great; I know you're nervous, but you're so well-rehearsed. Heck, I bet we'll have to drag you off that stage once you get started as you'll be having so much fun!"

The two smiled at each other as the audio man checked Maggie's mic. He moved back near the curtain, looked at Maggie and said, "I'm going to count down from five, then point to you, which will be your queue to walk out and start the introductions." She nodded.

Moments later, with the point of his finger, she walked onto the stage to launch the event. All of the women who were going to speak were now gathered around Colleen backstage, sharing praises about how well her mom was doing.

"She could easily quit her day job and take up public speaking!" Madeline exclaimed.

"My mom's incredible," Colleen replied. "I wouldn't be surprised if she decided to add public speaking to her resume."

The group heard Maggie queue the first lightning talk. "Our first lightning talk will be presented by two friends who will talk about a practice they call The Homework Assignment, that helped them change their careers and return to the workforce. Please welcome Claire Stanley and Bryn Miles."

The audience clapped, and Bryn gave Gloria's hand one last squeeze, "Thank you for coming backstage to wish me luck; it's so nice to see you again. By the way, I love that dress. It looks great on you," she said to the seamstress she met a few months earlier that now was her friend.

"Thank you," she replied. "I made it myself; green is my favorite color."

Bryn nodded and winked at her before walking on the stage with Claire. As the pair took their seats, Christine approached Claudia and Madeline from behind and, wrapping an arm around each of them, said, "This program will work. We're going to change lives," The three women nodded.

The woman in the green dress standing in front of them turned around, grinned and said, "You already have."

Acknowledgements

I've read that new writers often get carried away with verbose acknowledgments. I am happy to report that I qualify, as I'm incredibly grateful to a sea of amazing humans that have supported my efforts to publish this book - whether they know it or not.

First acknowledgment is to my family; Jon, Ryan, and Clay. You always knew that writing a book was a dream of mine, and in order to have the stories and experiences to write about and realize this dream, I was often away from home or unavailable due to a work commitment. Thank you for your love, support, and understanding when I couldn't be as present as I would have liked. I am grateful for our family unit.

Next, I would like to acknowledge the long list of women that have influenced my career journey and shaped many of the characters and stories in this book. Christine Bongard, Jennifer Didier, Heidi Lorenzen, Chaitra Vedullapalli and Lani Phillips - you are all such incredible leaders and thoughtful women, who leave me in awe of everything you do and how you do it. Thank you for your support, friendship, and love over the years. You all have elevated me to get to a point where I felt confident to create and share the stories in this book, and for that I will be eternally grateful. I especially want to thank you for the tough feedback you have provided me in the past, as even though it was hard to hear at the time, it made me a better professional and friend.

Now to the team at Maker Turtle, LLC. You made publishing this book and getting it into the hands of others a painless process. I can't thank you enough for your generosity and input regarding taking an idea and turning it into a reality.

Lastly to Jessica Hawk. It was our tough conversation over lunch where you challenged me to "land my plane and finish my sentence." That was a life-changing moment for me, and I thank you for all of your leadership, friendship, and love.

About the Author

Sharan Hildebrand is a 30-year corporate executive, speaker, and founder of Fearless Sisters, LLC. With a career built in technology, Sharan was motivated to form Fearless Sisters after observing the lack of female leadership in the industry.

Dedicated to elevating the next generation of female leader, Sharan loves to mentor and connect women with resources to advance their career journey.

Sharan is a lifetime native of the Chicago area, where she currently resides